CUTTING
THE TIES

Conquering Abuse

To Khristian,
An intelligent, talented
young man.
Thanks!

DN Dunbar
6/15/24

Gwendolyn Dunbar

CUTTING THE TIES
Conquering Abuse

Copyright © 2023 Gwendolyn Dunbar

ALL RIGHTS RESERVED

No part of this publication may be reproduced, stored in a retrieval system, or transmitted, in any form or by any means, electronic, mechanical, photocopying, recording or otherwise, without the express written permission of the author.

Contents

Preface

Experience is the best teacher. I am a teacher, a parent, a sister, and a daughter. As a child and throughout my adolescence, I thought that if I paid attention to the things happening around me, I would always make the right decisions. Why? Because I was smarter and I knew what was right and what could be the consequences of wrong choices. It didn't help matters when I grew up in a social environment that was just the opposite of me. I did my best not to make the same mistakes I saw others make. I remember often saying that I would make better decisions. Our differences would make us fight a lot. I would see family members go through depression over boyfriends and being abused. I heard of other family members outside my immediate household experiencing similar trauma. Sometimes the older family members would talk about how the same things happened to some of them when they were younger. The problem was that it was never that person's issue. They always talked about problems in life as someone else's. In reality, everyone will experience some kind of romantic drama if they are ever in a relationship. I was under the illusion that these things would never ever happen to me. I know better. I won't put myself in that situation; instead, I would leave, fight back, and outsmart them. However, God showed me something different. Theory, planning and assumptions don't work in real life. We all have to experience something in order to grow. When my time came, I wasn't as ready as I thought I would be. I didn't feel I had anyone to turn to until one day, a neighbor sat me down and gave me the facts of her life. She counseled me with the harsh truth, told me what to do to get out, and told me that God thought more of me than to have me live that way. With her help and the help of others, I finally understood that my life was worth more than what I was going through. I got out, and now, I want to help others through stories based on real-life situations and experiences.

What I had to learn the hard way was that although you will see and hear things in life, the question is, what do you understand? In the bible, Matthew 13 explains that you will grow when you see and hear with an understanding of His word. People are people, and some of our relationship problems are generational. It's not new. Abuse of all kinds has been around forever. Drug abuse has been around forever. Cheating, racism, sexism and ageism have been around throughout the centuries. The solution to curtailing the dramas of life is opening up and making the younger generation aware of the pitfalls and signs of life. There must be a way to teach the next generation that there are things they must be aware of to live a long and happy life. We must make them mindful of the signs that could lead to those toxic relationships. There is no perfect solution, but the seeds of awareness need to be planted. Seeing and hearing are only part of the preparation of awareness. People must have a moral understanding of life, and sometimes that comes with experience. Finally, we need to help young people trapped in these unhealthy partnerships by giving them an awareness of the difference between love and control, with hope and goals for their future; that understanding starts by listening and knowing the reality of good and bad relationships. This book is based on real women and the trauma they experience in relationships with their boyfriends and husbands. The stories are fictitious and designed to tell a story with a possible solution and comments. Also, there is straightforward advice to further demonstrate the existence of life after abuse. I want to share these experiences with you in hopes that it will prevent, make others aware or help others realize that they can live without the abuse they may be living with. I especially would like to target the younger women who may have the same mindset that I had growing up. With better insight and awareness of what life has to offer, maybe this will be one obstacle they can avoid. Thank you for your support.

Why Read 'Cutting All Ties?'

Why read *Cutting the Ties?* Years ago, when I was on a small income with a meager monthly check, I took the time to go to Kroch's and Brentano's bookstore to buy at least one book. Reading was my way of getting away from everything that was going on in my life. I learned so many things about life. The majority of my reading consisted of biographies and African American history books. I understood a world of people and places outside of my skimpy little existence. I learned about the struggles of Black people in America and about women in America, which led to a dream of promoting change one day. But that knowledge was not helpful because my life was not like the books I read. When I reached certain forks in the road, I made wrong decisions, and my dreams were either delayed or forgotten. I got into bad relationships. When I was working on getting out of a devastatingly horrible situation, I saw a student in eighth grade come to school with a black eye and other bruises on her face. She had been out of school for a few days. When she was questioned about her whereabouts, she said her 19-year-old boyfriend had done that to her. When asked to report it, she said no because she deserved it. She had taken some of his money, and the beating was the consequence of her action. It touched my heart because of similar situations, but I never felt I deserved it. This made me realize I needed to work more on removing myself from my position. I decided to do something to help young people by writing from my story and other older women's stories who made it out of abusive liaisons.

Telling these stories of domestic abuse demonstrates how men have released power, control, and domination on women for centuries. We received an abundance of changes in this world when women stood up during the Women's Rights Movement in the 1970s. Although, we are decades past that time, things still have been taken for granted and never fully changed. Young women need to know about past struggles and understand that they have to keep up the fight. Women are still being discriminated against in the workforce through unequal pay and chances for advancement. Women are still victims of sexual harassment at all levels of education, professions and status, as exhibited by the "Me Too Movement". The issue of second-class citizenship, abuse, and discrimination will always be forgotten if the awareness of this problem is not spoken about by older women, seriously and effectively, with younger women. I hope this book will be the first step to open up more conversations through mentoring. Hopefully, it will plant the seed of knowledge for a better future for the females of this world.

In order to stop the cycle of abuse for individuals, families and in society as a whole, we need to educate our young and older women to be aware of its signs and process. There are several avenues of abuse, such as controlling your every move and behavior; neglect, cheating, double standards, male privilege and isolation. Unless these things are discussed and addressed, women will continue to run in the same circle of the past, financially, spiritually, mentally and physically. Without some candid conversations, women will continue to suffer and think that they have to accept this as fate. We have to teach each other, not lecture, through becoming transparent, real lessons and stories to demonstrate that their vulnerabilities can turn into strengths. They need to see that there is a way out. By showing how people can overcome, maybe the seed of knowledge that can save a person's life.

Finally, this book will hopefully produce a better society for women today and for future generations. The goal is to prepare them financially secure and to go into relationships with a clear, observant, and conscious mind. In the beginning, there are charming words, actions, and promises that draw a woman in. Women are sometimes groomed by a man with such charm that when signs of abuse happen, they will overlook the obvious sudden mood changes, isolation, and rules. Many times, women blame themselves for causing these changes. These behaviors by men are signs of issues that can escalate. Women need to understand that the way you get into relationships can have an effect for the rest of their life. Women need to learn to wait and search for Dr. Right and not Dr. Right Now. Women need to learn to set long-term and short-term goals and not just follow the plans of others. Women need to be able to take care of themselves, and be aware of men who want to take care of them. Women need to beware when it's time to Cut All Ties by understanding that we all may experience some abuse but love ourselves first and see that there are brighter days outside of it.

Failure is Not an Option

Failure is not an option.
This is what I want you to see.
Life doesn't offer much.
And there are no guarantees
The opportunities are endless
And the chances of making it are limitless.
So the choice is for you to see.

Failure is not an option.
This is what they used to say.
If you put your best foot forth
Each and every day,
And count each step positively to reach your
goal,
You will step up the ladder of success as a
whole.
So the choice is for you to see.
Failure is not an option.
This is what they used to say.
If you make a mistake,

Learn from it and throw it away.
No one is perfect unless they are fake.
Look toward the future in a positive way
So the choice is for you to make.

Failure is not an option.
Remember this whenever you begin anew,
Never give up and always see things through.
Achievement and accomplishment are the
words to keep in mind.
Because victory and triumph are what you're
trying to find.
Just keep your mind focused and let some
things be
The choice is for you to see.

Jesus answered, "Even I do bear witness about myself, my testimony is true, for I know where I came from and where I am going. You know not where I come from or where I am going."

—*Johns 8:14*

The Testimony

(Be a woman who is willing to get back up and fight back no matter how tough times get)

It was one of those nights. The arguments lasted for hours and hours, the fear of what might happen next and wondering when this madness would stop while my anxiety peaked with confusion and uncertainty. It stopped the moment he was gone from my sight. The welcoming spirit of isolation seemed to be the

3

only refuge. I needed to get away from everyone. It was paralyzing as I passed by all the family members watching television. My steps led me to the top porch of the house in the middle of the night. Here, there were no disdain looks or questions like, "What's the matter with you?" "I told you to leave him alone!" or "She'll get enough after while!" The family did not hold back in giving their opinion and never a comforting word or response. They were quick to criticize but often had difficulty accepting it from others. I walked on, trying to hold back the tears while my mind was reviewing the disasters of my current circumstances. When I reached the top step, I just stared at the full moon and the brightness of the stars in the sky, praying to God. Finally, the silence broke; the misery could no longer be contained. I found myself speaking loudly through the stillness and silence of the night. I asked God for a way out of this mess. I asked for the strength and endurance to end this violent, cruel, controlling, and dead-end relationship. Then just as suddenly as it started, the words stopped and I felt exhausted. I slid down on the side of the railing of the porch; I put my hands over my face and held my head down. God must have recognized the urgency of my prayer because I began to hear a voice speak to me. It said, "All you have to do is to call and lean on me." As my head rose to the sky, I saw a door open. God spoke directly to me with these words, "He's gone and will not be back. Take this as a lesson and tell others your testimony."

After all is said and done, you made it through the hardest time of your life. Now what do you do? For women who have survived abusive relationships, this is a time for the rebirth of their lives. It's a second chance or just another chance in some cases. You have survived a controlling, powerless situation and now you are free. Well, not entirely, because the past keeps chasing you like a dog nipping at your heels as you try to forget. There are nightmares and bad memories. There is gossip that no matter how much time has passed, some people never let you forget. There are people around you who have no confidence in you and they never support you. With this entire trauma still hanging over your head, it's no wonder that you have a hard time seeking the help you need. But God expects us to give our testimony or to tell our story to help others. You may have experienced something so many women have gone through. How do some get out, survive, and gain ground? Some women are afraid. They have been killed or permanently damaged mentally, spiritually and/or physically. Your words can be an encouragement or hope to others who are afraid, contemplating leaving, or have left but are doubtful about their decision. This is a story of a woman who struggles to take that first step to heal herself by sharing her experience with others.

Day One: Monday

It was the first meeting of the season and the first time I had ever attempted to do anything like this before. I asked the Lord to make this night go smoothly. This was something that I had been waiting to do for the longest but dreaded. "Stop! Just stop it!" I had a mission to do, and I wasn't going to worry about it. By taking a deep breath, I consoled myself from such negative thoughts before heading into the group therapy session in a circle with women. "Oh my God! It's 7:00! Where are they? They should have been here by now." By taking another deep breath, I thought about the empty place, wondering if people might have left. I was convinced that I had gotten the time wrong until I realized, "Oh, my goodness. Today is Monday. We are supposed to meet on Tuesdays, damn!" It was hard enough for me to step out today and tomorrow really felt like an impossible task altogether. Today I talked to God and prayed silently because I try to keep them only for Him. But lately, I felt the urge to share my testimony with others. I have been blessed in so many ways and I don't want to just share the good news, but every little bit of it that led up to it.

Day Two: Tuesday

Tonight was finally the night. Yet here I was again, drowned in doubt and confusion, thinking I would bore everyone with my story. Neither did I want anyone to infuriate me. I would want to avoid getting into a fight tonight. I told Jennie that I was going to give my testimony tonight. She asked me about it, and I told her, "Just be there." I wanted Jennie to hear what I had to say with all the others, and I needed her for moral support.

I felt good tonight. I wanted everybody to understand that although things could be at an all-time low, we have to find something to laugh at. This testimony is something that I felt God wanted me to pass on my story and help others realize that there is life after tragedy. The urge to vocalize this idea through my story was strong, and I just hoped everybody would be receptive enough.

Day Two: Tuesday Night - 6:00 PM

I got here a little early to settle myself before others. I was apprehensive, so I got up and set the chairs in a circle. I started straightening up other things, like picking up pieces of paper from the floor. Every few minutes, I would walk over to the window to see if anybody was pulling up. Still, no one. I feared that they wouldn't show up. I realized that I was early and that the meeting wasn't due to start until seven. I grabbed a magazine from the rack and attempted to read but found myself only flipping through the pages. I just put it down. Just then, I heard a loud screech. I thought it was Regina with her raggedy four-door Chevy. I looked out of the window. Nope, it was some young teenager who had lost control of his car and was trying not to hit that crazy cat from across the street. I checked my watch and realized only twenty minutes had passed. "See, this is why I never try to be early." I can't stand waiting on anything or anybody. Finally, I convinced myself to take a seat and lay my head on the table for a short nap.

Day Two: Tuesday Night - 8:00 PM

"Oh my God! What time is it?" It was mighty quiet in here. The time was 8 o'clock. I sat up and looked around the room, realizing people might have been here. But that couldn't be because I was sure to have heard something. I stood up and stretched every part of my body, holding my head back while reaching for the ceiling on my tip-toes. That felt good. I noticed that all the seats were out of order. I pondered if somebody else had come by, a thief maybe. I became nervous and started to look for my purse. I tried to smile out of my anxious state. I didn't know why I was looking for my purse since it wasn't of any value, nor the contents inside. As I turned around to leave, I saw a note on the table next to where I was sleeping that read, "Hey, girl. You were sleeping so well. We just didn't have the heart to wake you. See you next time." I was disappointed. I read it again to make sure what it said. I couldn't believe that they left me there. I walked out slowly and mumbled to myself, "I'll do it next week."

Next Week: Tuesday Night - 7:15 PM

I made a promise to myself to be on time. Well, of course, I was late about 10-15 minutes and they had already started talking. I wanted to be first. I took a seat and breathed. Those deep breaths didn't help, so I closed my eyes to relax. When I opened them, everyone was staring at me. I was flushed within seconds from this staggering gaze. I quietly apologized and sat on my hands to further calm myself down. Glenda was speaking about an episode she had with a family member that resulted in a big brawl with her in-laws and siblings. It was interesting, but she was a bit long-winded with her story. I knew I could tell mine better. I built my confidence with this scenario. When she finished, they asked if anyone else would like to share. I was about to speak up when I felt a strange feeling in my gut that went up to my throat. I couldn't calm down my nerves, so I just sat there and didn't say anything.

My friend Joyce began sharing her story about her fear of cats. She explained her slow recovery from this phobia. Joyce's boyfriend used her phobia to keep her in line. He would belittle and taunt her with the cat in the room. She unfolded that her boyfriend began to force Joyce to touch the cat while he was still in the arms of her boyfriend. Next, she allowed the cat to walk around the room. With each stage of the process, she became a little more comfortable with the cat, but it was the forcefulness and the demeanor of her boyfriend that took away all the real glory of getting over the fear. Eventually, the fear became a little more tolerant but never disappeared. The story didn't have a happily ever after effect because her boyfriend used the cats to keep her under his control. The only part I remember is that Joyce overcame her fear. I realized that if she could adjust her fears, I could overcome mine. I felt better and more confident to speak. My mind kept telling me, "I can do this next time." But I decided to fight that feeling and stood up to make sure that everyone knew that it was my time to speak. I had convinced myself that this was it. I looked around at everyone. I could feel that burning sensation in my stomach, but I ignored it. I said to myself, "Lord, give me strength and please don't let them laugh or look down on me. Please allow me to speak the words you would have me to say." Suddenly, the words began to spill out of my mouth. I began to tell the testimony I had been rehearsing so many times and in different voices. My voice was shaky, slow and low in the beginning.

"I have wanted to tell somebody my story for a long time. Just to share. I have often felt that maybe my story will help someone else in this room with their problem," still shaking, I started to walk around and continued, "I have gone through some terrible times in my life. Only by the grace of God did I escape. Abuse is a well-known part of my life from childhood into adulthood. I have been beaten up and torn down mentally, physically, and spiritually. The worse episode happened when I was seven months pregnant. I was an hour late getting back to my man's apartment one summer afternoon. I knew it was a mistake to be late, so I drove as fast as I could to try not to be any later than I already was. My mind was racing. I really felt that I should have gone back home. I got out of the car and walked as quickly as I could. I approached the building. I glanced at the second-floor corner window to see if he was watching. There was no sign. Maybe I was worrying over nothing, I thought. The elevator came right away, and I went to the second floor. As I walked down the hallway, it felt like I was walking a whole block. Something was urging me to turn around and go home, but I blindly kept going. He opened the door. I looked at him, and my voice trembled as I went on. As I walked through the door. He was furious and high. He started yelling about this man he claimed I was seeing. 'You went to see James, didn't you? Tell the truth, and we can let this go.' He was pacing in front of me as I sat petrified on the couch. I kept telling myself I shouldn't have come. I knew I had to find a way to get out of there. Just then, I realized it was too late. I told him the truth, stating that I had gone home and stopped at Sheila's house on the way back. That made matters worse. He began screaming about Sheila being a dike and assumed that I, who was seven months pregnant, may be participating in some homosexual activity with Sheila and her friend. The whole idea was ridiculous. I didn't care at this point and I started telling him how stupid it was. In the midst of it all, he slapped me so hard that my head fell back against the wall. The fear of what could happen to my baby ran across my mind and I tried to think of a way out. I figured that the only way to get away from all the madness was to calm the situation down, but the more I tried the worse things got." I was surprised with myself to explicate the next part of this story, "He was high and in an uncontrollable state. Suddenly, he came up with the most horrible and nastiest thing that I could ever imagine. He grabbed my pants and pulled them off. He pulled my legs apart and jabbed his fingers inside me, took his fingers out and looked at them. He slapped me again. He claimed that the discharge he felt was semen. Then he climbed on top of me and repeatedly slapped me, I don't know how many times. I was baffled and crying, I couldn't do anything. Then he stopped. He apologized for his behavior and blamed me for it. He said that I should not have lied to him. He got off and I saw my opportunity. Although I didn't have my pants on, I ran as fast as I could, down the hall. When he saw that I had gotten out, he came after me and caught me. I screamed but no one came to my aid. I fought to get away, but he dragged me by my legs and pulled me back to the apartment. I couldn't fight anymore. I felt defeated behind the locked door. The only thing he said was 'Why did you do that?' The puzzling piece about this was that he truly did not understand why. Fortunately, the police came. He tried to tell them that nothing was wrong but they could see things differently. I was taken away from there and put in the hospital. My face was swollen on the left side, and a black eye." Towards the end, I shared a hopeful precedent of my story, "Since that time, I have grown. God has placed it on my heart to pass the message on to all women old and young that He will pull you through. Things could have been worst. The secret is to be prayerful and know that He is always by your side. Just ask for His help, guidance and wisdom. He will look after you. Circumstances such as this can change the victim's life. So many women never recover, some even die. It took me a while to get away from this relationship totally, and there were other episodes to this story. But tonight, my message to you is that I recovered and I thank God because he got me out of one of the most horrific times in my life. Thank you for allowing me to share."

The mood of the circle was quiet and shocked because I had never told them anything about myself. No one expected a story like this from me. I was well-dressed, professional, and soft-spoken. No one said a word. In fact, throughout my whole testimony, no one moved. I was glad for the attentive audience, but I was uncomfortable about how they might feel about me afterwards but I continued on by sharing other details about the two deaths in my family and there was the loss of respect from family members. In addition, I told the circle about my loss of my self-esteem, self-respect, and confidence; and it made me lose focus on the important people in my life. Emotionally, I still had not recovered.

This was the only way I have ever been able to tell this story without feeling people's judgment. I remembered that when I finally got out of the hospital I never turned back to him. I never returned to him. On the other hand, I had a healthy, beautiful and understanding son. I kept my job and took care of my sons; and managed to further my education.

Anyways, I ended my talk on a lighter note, "I didn't mean to make this story so long. But don't feel bad for me because my biggest news that I would to share now is that summer is over but I am proud to say that-I DIDN'T GET NO MOSQUITO BITES ALL SUMMER."

Surprised by the ending of my testimony, all the women fell out laughing. That statement broke the tension in the room. There was time for one other person to confess to the problems plaguing her, life then the group broke up.

God told me to share that story. I was nervous and unsure about telling it even after it was over. As I was walking out to my car, Joyce, the 18 years old, asked if she could speak to me for a moment. She cried as she told the real story. She didn't feel comfortable enough to talk to the group. Her problem was similar to mine and many other women in the group. She was confused about what to do until she heard my story. Joyce thanked me because now she knew she was doing the right thing by staying away. We encouraged each other and exchanged phone numbers. I told her to call me if she was ever in need.

Day Four - Next Tuesday Night - 7:00PM

I was late for the meeting again. I sat quietly and listened to the stories of other women and applauded. Joyce stood and told her story. I was so proud of her for having the courage, especially when she mentioned that my words helped her to make the right decisions to change her life. Now I know why God wanted me to give my testimony.

Comments:

Physical abuse is the ultimate and most horrendous form of abuse. It is usually the first type of abuse that people think of when the subject comes up. It is what all the other forms of abuse can lead to. To experience it is even more atrocious because it is something you will always remember. Ask any victim about their first time or their worst time and usually, they are able to tell every detail from beginning to end. It affects you mentally and spiritually. Mentally, you are anxious, nervous, and always aware of the triggers or wondering if or when it will ever end. Your life is at the mercy of the abuser's mood of the day. Spiritually, you can lose all hope and confidence. Living through a physically abusive relationship is like living through a nightmare; the bully has the advantage over you in many cases.

Physical abuse is what most people think about when you mention the word abuse. The picture that always crosses the mind of a person is someone with a black eye or bruises on their body. This image is consistently being viewed on television programs. Someone pointing in your face, someone spitting on you, someone shaking you up and grabbing your arm and lastly, someone hitting you with their hands or anything else they choose to use. I am speaking from the heart. If you get nothing else from this, listen to this one bit of advice regarding any form of abuse, especially physical. If it happens once, you can bet it will happen again. The pain doesn't get better. It gets worse each time. It doesn't just hurt physically. It is like a roller coaster. In the beginning, you start off well, but as you continue to go on, tension builds. Then as you reach the top, you are attacked. Now you are on the way down-things are simmering, and you hear all the apologies. You are doing fine for a while until, out the blue, it starts over again.

One of the first steps to getting out of an abusive situation is by acknowledging that you are in one. Once you have realized that the situation is not healthy for you, you can clear your mind and find ways to change your circumstances. It's not an easy path for anyone caught in this trap. The abuser does not give up easily. The trend goes from apologizes to intimidation, from blaming you to finding ways to make you feel sorry for their condition or stalking you. There are no certain patterns or rules for the abuser because every individual is different and the circumstances of relationships vary. You could live in the fantasy that the first time will be the last time but nine times out of ten, it won't. You may say that it won't be you because you will fight back or kill them. Why put yourself and your life through that trauma for a person who wants to hurt you? Another point is that abusive actions from a person are not about love-its about power and control. When you get that threatening feeling, follow your first mind. The key factor here is when you find yourself under the powerful thumb of a harmful person, pray for space, clarity, freedom and peace; find your way out; and finally share your testimony with those who need it.

Codependency

Yeah, she was one of them.
One of them who was codependent
I'm glad she got over him.
I'm glad she got away from him.
She was a victim of codependency.

What is codependency?
It is a disease of guilt that you can't see.
It's a mind thing.
It develops with at least two people holding a
ring.
It develops when the problems of one
Takes over the ring for both.
Then only sadness is all she wrote.
It begins with the dependent one who, in the
past, may have been happy and gay.
But now he needs lots more of love and help
every day.
It may be because of drugs.
It may be depression or that mental illness bug.
It may be selfishness.
It may be for power, control, or helplessness,
It doesn't matter because the dependent one

is the one who relies on another.

The codependent, on the other hand,
Tries hard to keep things wrapped up with
something as thin as a rubber band.
It may be that she feels she is fulfilling a void
in life.
It could be that she is only doing what is right.
It may be due to low self-esteem.
It may be because she feels she is fulfilling
God's dream.
It may be because she feels she can straighten
things out.
Or it could be that she feels she can put him on
the right route.
As time passes, she discovers that she has
become powerless.
But it doesn't matter because the codependent
one is in a state of total helplessness.
How can you help the dependent one?
Whose single-focused mind looks at the
codependent as the one.
The one who is the blame for everything.
The one who is never complimented for
anything.

The only one who the dependent one relies
upon.
The only one who the dependent one schemes
on.
It's hard when the codependent begins to see
behind their opened eye.
It's hard when they finally realize,
That the dependent one
Only cares about number one.

When in this situation, you give and support
until your insides rot.
You think that you are helping, but you are
not.
Your brain and your heart tell you have to
help, but your mind becomes a blank slot.

When the pressure gets too tough, what do
you do?
You tried to leave, but he cries.
You try to talk it out but all you hear are well-
intention lies.
Your feelings are pulled like a roller coaster.
On one hand, you are angry because of the
abuse.

Being slapped, being told that you are of no
use.

On the other hand, you feel sorry because he
tried to commit suicide
You fear he could've died.
You feel these things would be different if you
had just realized.
Then like a lightning bolt, the thought comes
into your head
That this is not going to stop until one of you is
dead.
You finally concluded,
That the only way out is for you to be
excluded.
You have to find a way out of this terrible
dream.

The only way out is to break the ring and join
another team.
At last, a book or a friend tells you that
everyone is responsible for themselves.
But it still doesn't click
Then you get in a troublesome situation
yourself

The problem comes when now "you need help," and you don't get any help quick. No one, not even the dependent one, helps a lick.

So, with all your will-
I mean, it took every second, every minute, and every hour.
I know to many this may seem odd,
But it took the help of faith and trust in God.
You see, the codependent one realizes that in order to get out is with God's help.
Because the dependent one had made you lose yourself.

"Love is patient and kind; love does not envy or boast; it is not arrogant or rude. It does not insist on its' own way; it is not irritable or resentful."

—*Corinthians 13:4-5*

Today Is a New Day

Today is a new day! I was happy that I finally saw the light. I just made eighteen and I was a grown woman now. I didn't have to listen to my mother, and I have a man who is willing to do whatever he can to take care of me. I loved it. I got married because my father said if I got pregnant in his house, I had to leave. My mother and I believed him. I got pregnant and I knew that the next step was to get married. He didn't find out until the week of the wedding, which we had in the house. So, what? I wanted to leave that house anyway. They had too many rules and too many kids. All I needed was a man of my own, and I got him with Matthew. I knew it the day I saw him in the lunchroom at school. Oh my God, he was oh so fine. He had a pretty color skin, pretty wavy hair, and was just the right height. He dressed sharply and had beautiful eyes. But most of all, he had a gold tooth in the front of his mouth. It seemed like every girl in the school had eyes on him. I sat up straight, put on my best smile and switched ever so seductively past him just so I could get his attention. I knew he was it for me, so I made sure that a friend of his introduced us. He could not resist me and I surely couldn't resist him. That was the beginning of our relationship, and it was at that point that we saw each other on a regular basis.

My mother was not pleased by this and started trying to put down her rules on me. She was only trying to make me do what she thought was best. But I always had a rebellious attitude toward my controlling mother. I knew what I wanted and was simply tired of her rules; I couldn't take it anymore. I would sneak out or stay out as long as I wanted. I would leave for school but never make it to the door of the school. I would yell, cry, and cause all kinds of havoc in the house to get my way. Daddy was not informed because my mother didn't want him to kill me. She tried whipping me, punishing me and talking to me, but when all else failed, she relied on, "This is my house and you will follow my rules." So, I ran away. I didn't get far because I didn't have any money. Matthew told me how stupid an idea that was. After this, we went to counseling and with some compromising, my mother loosened the reign a little bit. This is when I got pregnant. I thought it was the best thing because now I am on my own.

Our marriage was perfect at first because we had each other. We had gotten an apartment on Westside. It was a studio, but that's all we needed. He dropped out of school and got a job. He was there with me every step of the way. I had the baby, which was a beautiful girl. Many of the things I liked about myself and Matthew were reflected in her. We loved her so much. Then things began to change. He lost his job and began hustling to get money. Many times, the bills weren't paid, and I had to ask my mother for money. I have always been a fighter. In fact, my reputation throughout my school had been for fighting for myself and taking up for others, no matter what. I was getting tired of asking my mother for help, so the arguments between us became frequent. One day I looked through his pockets when he went to sleep after staying out half the night and found a wad of money. I tried to wake him up, but he ignored me. I shook him, and he still tried to ignore me. Finally, I stood on top of the bed, climbed on top of his back and jumped up and down on his back. That woke him up and we started fighting. I was all over him, and he just kept trying to stop me. Finally, he wrestled me down, but he had to sit on me to stop me. He picked up the phone and called my mother and told her he couldn't do it anymore. He asked her to come and get me. I didn't care because after a year, the honeymoon was over, and I was done with him. I knew he was cheating on me anyway, so I started cheating on him. In addition to that, he had started getting high and I found out that that's where our money was going.

Isn't life great? After all my heartaches, I decided there was no need to tie myself down to one person. After all, I am a beautiful black woman who has a lot to offer a man. Why limit myself to one person? My problem was that I never set a goal list of what kind of man was best for me. Finally, I found John. John was the love of my life. He was a college basketball player. He was handsome and had a lot more to offer me. With John, I definitely see much more than Matthew could have ever given me. I fell head over heels in love with him. We kept in touch while he was away at school. He offered me the world. He had the potential to become a professional ball player, and I wanted to be right there with him, along with my daughter. Before the year was out, he dumped me for a woman who he felt was more suitable for his taste. I felt used and went into depression. I tried to kill myself, and I made those who loved me most feel my pain. I had never been without a man since I was thirteen and I wasn't prepared this time. I loved him and I thought he loved me. If I had known he was planning to leave, I would've prepared myself and gotten another man. This was a learning moment for me. Never again will I be left abandoned.

I'm twenty-one now and life is great. I found two men this time and they both adored me. I decided to change the way I did things about myself to keep my men. I did whatever it took to keep them. They didn't know about each other. They may have suspected that I was in more than one relationship, but they had no proof. Ricky was a street hustler. At the time, I was working in the neighborhood store to make extra money. One day, he got into trouble and needed money to pay some people off. I told Ricky about the owner and about how much he trusted the keys with me. We decided to rob the place. We didn't get caught, but, needless to say,

I lost that job. I dropped Ricky because I realized how dumb that was, and I wasn't willing to go to jail for anyone.

Frank was a drug dealer and he usually had lots of money, so I kept seeing him. I ignored the warning signs. All I knew was that he loved me, but he required a lot of attention. I was willing to ignore all the danger signs because of his attentiveness to me and I needed that. However, one thing after another came to the surface and I found one excuse after another to justify his actions. For instance, one day, my daughter said Frank touched her in the wrong place, but I didn't believe her because she had a tendency to lie. He wanted his dinner ready whenever he came in with no excuses. That was no problem because I knew what I had to do to keep him. We would stay locked in the room for hours doing what adults do. Even to the point of ignoring family members, even my daughter. That didn't matter because I knew Frank enjoyed my company; I needed this man and he satisfied all my needs. The tide changed when one day, I found out that he was at his cousin's house with another woman. The house was about five blocks away. I took that walk with thoughts of confronting them in a way he never expected. As I approached the house, they saw me coming and wouldn't open the door after I knocked. Infuriated, I began to bang louder and louder on the door, yelling, "I know your ass is in there with that bitch. Come on out!" Finally, Frank walked out and said let's go. He walked past me and never looked at me as if he didn't want to be seen with me. I started cussing at him as he walked ahead of me. That didn't get his attention, so I started picking up whatever I saw and threw it at him. He continued walking. When I picked up a can and it hit Frank in the back of his head, he turned on me and started beating me mercilessly. When he finished, I had two broken ribs, a black eye and severe pains in the back of my head. That was the end of Frank and me. The next day the police mysteriously got a tip on a drug pickup, and he was arrested for trying to sell drugs. In addition, his drug supplier reported him to the police because he had stolen some of his product.

I am thirty-one now and life is grand. I have two children now and my own apartment in City Housing. After that last beating, I started having seizures. This qualified me to receive SSI. In addition, I had never divorced Matthew, so when he was shot and killed during a robbery, we now received benefits from him. I can live happily and free. The men in my life have come and gone and I tend to get very depressed when I go through a break-up. On the other hand, whenever there is a man in my life, I feel so beautiful and complete. I needed a man who I could grow with and one to help support my children and me. I wanted a complete family. I began thinking that my kids were getting out of control and I needed help. My mother wants to, but she gets in too much of my business.

My new man, Reginald, can help with bills, satisfy me and help with my kids. In the meantime, life has continued to go on. My daughter had serious issues with the new rules and the adjustments to Reginald. She rebelled against the changes in discipline, restrictions and rules coming from a person that she considered a stranger in her house. We have been clashing continuously. My son, who is my heart, has tantrums that I am having difficulty controlling. Reginald has really been firm with them, which is what they both need. However, I didn't realize that that firmness included me too. The freedom my children and I had dwindled down from 100 to 30. After a while, we all were under his rule of thumb. The kids were told to make no detours after school. None of us were allowed to have company, not even family members. Chores were assigned. If any of his rules were disobeyed, you suffered the raft of Reginald. This meant physical, verbal, and mental abuse from beatings, belittling comments, severe punishments and isolation.

The results devastated my family. My daughter and my son's issues with Reginald's abusive behavior have not been resolved. It seemed like every time I complained about his methods of control, Reginald would remind me that I told him this was what I needed him to do. We argued continuously, not just about them but about us. He didn't want me to be with my family. He wanted me to come straight home and attend to his needs. Financially the well had run dry because he was a seasonal construction worker and didn't always have money to contribute to the household but wanted to control the funds that came in. He had more access to my children's time because he began to watch the household while I was at work. My friends and family were now estranged and alienated from us.

After several years of one tragedy after another, I decided it was time to move on. I had hit my limit. Reginald sensed the change in me and started trying to monitor my movement more and more, but he wasn't able to keep up. This is when I found Carl. Carl and I found ways to meet up regardless of the obstacles of

Reginald. Carl and I devised a plan to get rid of Reginald. I found another apartment and transferred my son to another school. I purposely paid no rent and told the landlord that I would be moving. One day when I knew Reginald would be away, Carl, my family, and friends helped us to move out. That day I discovered this was right in the nick of time. We found guns hidden in every room we cleaned out. There were guns hidden in the hamper, in the closet, in the kitchen cabinets, and hidden under my mattress. Right then, it dawned on me, Reginald had always told me that he would kill me before he would ever let me go. To this day, I am grateful to God for giving me a way out.

The experience had a big impact on my mind and definitely made me rethink my life. Carl and I got married and started working toward improving our status in life. Carl was different. He was also from the streets but had experiences that took him in another direction. He was all about the money and working hard to get it. I felt it in my heart he was finally the one. I loved Carl, but he loved a lot of women and had seven other children with baggage. He was a D.J. at night and worked for the city in the daytime. Even though Carl worked in a small family lounge, he had quite a following and reputation with needy, lonely, and single female patrons. But he always put me first, and the other women knew it. He cheated, but he took care of me and my children. For instance, there was the time that he took my so-called best friend to Vegas for the weekend and I found the evidence in the car. I confronted him with it and we fought over and over about it. I went to my friend's house, ready to fight her, but she wouldn't open the door. There were also problems with Carl's children coming through now and then, showing favoritism towards his children.

After so many problems, we moved to Texas to escape the issues we were having. But you know people are people, and it doesn't matter where they go, if they want to do something, it will be done. I finally had to let things go because the fighting began to wear on me physically. I started experiencing uncontrollable pain in my head, back and abdomen. I started having seizures again as a result of stress and the kick in the head by Frank years ago. I had to quit my job and apply for public assistance. When Carl decided to leave, I started to feel better about myself.

I started seeing a therapist because even though I began to feel better, I was lonesome. I blamed myself for all the problems I was having over the years. Why is it that I could not keep a man? Why is it that I can't have that happy family with the man I love? Why is it that I can't just have the companionship that will be a happily ever after, fairy tale life that will last till death do us part? Most importantly, I began to question why I felt that I needed a man to validate my life. As these questions crossed my mind and the therapy continued, I realized that God brought me into this world alone and the only person I need is Him. I began to see that I had done nothing with my life but jump from one relationship to another and had not given God a chance to send the right guy into my life. I decided to relax and release all of my pain and tension, and decided to let go and let God take control of my life. I decided to let all my energy go toward who could help me the most - God. I began to pray more; attend church and participate in community activities that would take my mind off all the negative vibes of my life. Gradually, I forgot my problems and started to focus on helping others.

Through many sessions with my therapist, I discovered I was running around looking for love when I really didn't love myself enough. During one session, my therapist asked me, "What is self-love?" she told me that my assignment for the next session was to think about how much I love myself. I looked it up and found-self-love means regard for one's own well-being and happiness. I began to think that I have always looked for someone else to love and adore me as an expression of my self-worth.

Then I looked up self-worth. Having a sense of self-worth means that you value yourself, and having a sense of self-value implies that you are worthy. Self-worth is defined by Merriam-Webster as: "a feeling that you are a good person who deserves to be treated with respect." Suddenly, it became clear why I was having these issues with all these different men. My family consisted of a mother and a father, along with nine brothers and sisters. I was the oldest. My parents at first doted on me but later didn't have enough time for me. I needed someone to love, compliment, and encourage me. I didn't get enough of it in my household as a child and thought this was how to fulfill that void. I felt like I had discovered the invention of the century! I started to check myself, the people I was around, and the places I went to. I would look in the mirror every morning, telling myself that I was beautiful, intelligent and that nothing is too good for me. In addition, I began to respect myself more and would respond to positive things.

The therapist suggested that I work with young people exhibiting the beginning signs of the problems I had been through. We organized a group called Facing the Challenges of Relationships (FCR). We visited shelters. We talked in groups and/or with individual partners who were young and old. We took trips. We mainly tried to expose them to the world and the different things life offers. Our discussions ranged from abuse to education to self-love. The major premise was to help young people understand that some problems in life are not new; to establish a positive dialog with someone who has been through similar problems. Also, help them understand that they need to love and provide for themselves first; and, finally, realize that if they ever do find themselves going the wrong way, they can remember their options in order to get away.

After years of working with the young ladies and seeing some of them grow to be successful, proud, productive, and respectful citizens, I felt that I had achieved what God wanted me to do.

I was now more relaxed and secure in my life without a man. Just as I had completely let go of that desire, God sent me the man who he wanted me to be with. We have been together for ten years and are perfect for each other. Now I knew what my calling was. I needed to experience some of life's challenges in order to help others. Now I know that we have to be patient and wait on God before jumping to be with the first man to come our way. Finally, now I could proudly say, "Today is a new Day." May God bless and love you every day!

Comments:

Many times, young people have an unclear view of what it means to be an adult. They equate adulthood with freedom of choice. Young ladies, such as the one in this story, often say, "I'm grown, and I can do what I want to do!" you will find some young ladies who think that once they reach that magic age, it is instant adulthood. Freedom will sometimes get you into one disastrous relationship after another due to not taking the time to learn about your mate. Doing what you want can lead to unhealthy, reckless, and unplanned life choices. Being patient in your choices and following God's lead will more likely develop into a more informed partnership. So, don't push your agenda first, pray and listen to God's whispers. His plan is better than anything you could ever hope for. In essence, don't rush-prepare; think things through, and observe all you need to see before jumping into a relationship. Most importantly, you have to love yourself first in order to love others before you bring others into your life.

One More Chance

Give them another chance
Give them another chance
I did.
And another and another
It didn't work out for this mother.
It was part of his game.
It was part of his way to make you look lame.

We had been disagreeing for some time.
I knew he was up to something,
But I couldn't read between the lines.
I prayed for him, and I looked out for him.
But the results were the same.
He lied, and he cheated while continuing to
play the game.
We talked, and it was explained.
Then the final decision was arranged.
The relationship will now be hinging on
following the plan.
YOU HAVE ONE MORE CHANCE!
That chance didn't last.

My husband got off work at four but came in
at ten
Each time he was late, we argued, and each
time, he'd win.
Each time he was asked to leave, each time
turned on the romance.
He would beg and plead to get him another
chance.
I did.
Another time, at three in the morning, the door
opened, and in he pranced.
Drunk and out of his head,
He blamed it on the friends he had.
You felt torn.
Your heart tells you not to put him out because
he has no place to go
Your mind tells you stop and let him go solo.
You want to say you used up your one more
chance.
But you give in to him once more and say,
"Good night!"

This cheating man came home late one night.
After being gone six months, he smiled and
said he didn't want to fight.

He claimed it was my fault, and he said he
accepted my apology.
After you don't say anything, he felt relief but
didn't know the reality
As he sat down and told me to relax.
You looked at him and didn't say a thing.
In the back of my mind, these were the words
that you began to sing.
He can do whatever he wants to do while he
walks the floor.
In three months, he will be out the door.
The divorce papers are on the way.
Then see what he has to say.
Because he had used up all chances.

"Cast your burdens on the Lord, and He will sustain you: He will never permit the righteous to be moved."

—Psalms 55:22

Glory's Story

Love is a complicated thing. You could be the strongest, most intelligent person ever, but when it comes to love, life, and your decisions, love can make you look like the biggest fool ever. The difference between men and women can have a lot to do with just how big a fool you'll be. Men look at women as prey. In their minds, women are here on this earth to be conquered for their own use, whether for sex, cooking, cleaning, financial reasons, or just to boost their egos. They will take all kinds of risks to fulfill their male fantasies without even a bit of remorse or regret. Men think with two heads-their top head and the one down below. Once either or both of those two are satisfied, everything else is secondary. On the flip side, many women are looking for security. They rely on their feelings and their hearts. They want a man who will make them feel safe and trustworthy. They want a strong man who will be there for them, make them feel secure and good about themselves. Many times, women go overboard, making sacrifices financially and psychologically in the name of love. Such is the case with Glory. As I listened to her story, it saddened me to realize how many Glorys we have today. There are young women who tend to fall for the manipulation of men. It is amazing the lengths that so many females will go to just to get a man who only uses them for his own selfish reasons. Glory loved hard, so she did everything she should not have done. But there are times the love bug gets you, no matter how hard you try to stay away from it.

Glory sat in her recliner chair and gazed out the window of her two-bedroom apartment.

The sun was setting, and the moon was coming up with a bright yellow glow around it. It was such a calm day and Glory was exhausted from a long day at her factory job. Life was hard for her now as she reflected on her childhood. She was born and raised in Chicago in the year 1973. Her mother was killed by Glory's father after he accused her of being unfaithful. The rife was further enhanced when his wife found out anonymously that he was cheating on her. The accusations, the inconsistencies, and his controlling ways were the final straw. One day, Glory's mother left, and for several months there was no communication whatsoever. The frustration and disrespect the father felt led him to the most devastating final moments of both of their lives. He found out where the mother lived and waited by her car. When the mother walked through the parking lot, she spotted her husband too late. He shot her and then shot himself. Tears ran down Glory's face as the vivid image entered her mind. Now, she's without her mother and father at age ten.

Recognizing the trauma that Glory experienced, her aunts and grandmother doted over every aspect of her life as time passed

It was a quiet Saturday night and Glory's only day to rest. Glory was well set on staying in the house and watching television on this beautiful summer night. It had been a long week of struggles. Because she was a factory worker making minimum wage, a high school dropout and a single parent, she could barely make ends meet. One way she managed financially was to work overtime during the week. She got herself a glass of rum and coke to relax as she began flipping channels. Nothing seemed to catch her interest. She loved comedies but was bored of sitcoms because of their predictability, and she couldn't find a good movie. She put the remote down and closed her eyes, trying simply to relax. The more she tried, the harder it became; she was restless. Every time she tried to close her eyes, it was as if there was an automatic reflex on them because they would pop right back open. She was bored and anxious, so she gave up and tried to find something else to do. Right at that moment, the phone rang. Betty wanted to go to the neighborhood bar for a drink. Not sure this was a good idea, Glory agreed to go because she convinced herself to get out.

They met at Reggie's on Chicago's Westside around ten. The neighborhood was not the best, but everybody who was who went there. Generally, there were no problems unless somebody was messing with someone else's spouse. Betty and Glory came in and sat at the bar. Betty was a regular customer and knew the bartender, Richard. They even had been going out a few times. Glory, still bored, realized that Betty was only trying to get back with Richard, so she sat there quietly, glaring at the mirror behind all the rows of liquor. This was when Glory noticed a man by the name of Sam sitting at the end of the bar staring at her. She turned to look at him out of curiosity and received a big smile in return. He raised his glass in a friendly gesture and offered to buy her a drink. Glory accepted, and Sam walked over to sit by her. They introduced themselves to each other and began to drink and talk together, with her back now to Betty and Richard. The night flew by because she truly enjoyed the lively conversation and laughter. This night led to many more dates and time spent together. Although Glory, at the time, didn't want a relationship, all things seemed to flow in that direction.

They decided to take things slowly. Glory felt that her daughter was nearly grown and she didn't want to expose her to men outside her father. This really meant she did not want any men around because her children's fathers had long gone. Sam wasn't exactly straightforward about his reasons. The only thing he acknowledged was that he needed to resolve some issues with another relationship. Sam was married but told Glory that he was in the process of getting a divorce. Every time they met, he would complain about all the changes she was putting him through. The truth was Sam loved his wife and would never leave her.

As the years passed by, Glory joined the church but continued on the road of denial with Sam. In her heart, she always believed that he would leave his wife for good and marry her. One day out of the blue, Sam ran into the house and said he had a surprise for her. He had hit the lottery and found a house that he wanted her to move into with him. He never said but indicated that he and his wife's relationship had run its' course. He even showed her the paper where he would begin the divorce proceeding. However, as always, Sam kept an underlining factor from her that he did not want to talk about immediately. Glory was so overjoyed because her dreams were finally coming true and God had answered her prayers. You see, God may have been giving Glory what she wanted but remember, there are usually consequences that come along with it. Glory had been dealing with this married man for years and he never changed his ways. Now he comes with this. Glory was suspicious and for a good reason. The hitch was that Sam wanted Glory to sign her name on the house because he had bad credit.

He took her by the house and boosted her hopes even more. He really talked the game to get her right where he wanted her. She told all of her family and friends. There was nothing or no way you could have burst this bubble of happiness. They signed the papers and moved into a three-bedroom brick house with a finished basement. Glory and Sam went shopping for furniture for the entire house. They stayed together as any happy couple would for years. Although, there was no complete bliss in this household because Sam would occasionally disappear for months at a time, but he always paid the bills. He also made sure that all the bills were in his name. After some time passed, he started distancing himself from Glory. Not only was he leaving for long periods, but now when he was home, he required his own space. He seldom made time for them to be together and would stay in the basement and tell her he needed to be alone in his man cave.

Things really changed after Glory lost her job. Now she could no longer help out financially. Sam warned her that she would have to get a job or find somewhere else to live. Glory didn't have any skills and/or the know-how of what to do to get another job. Months passed by and Glory still had no success in her job hunt. One day after spending a day at the unemployment office, she walked into the house to discover that all her bags had been packed and a note from Sam saying she had to leave that day. Glory called multiple times. They argued, and Glory told Sam she had no place to go. Later, Sam informed Glory that she had to move out because his wife would be there by the end of the week. She asked about the house. The house title had been changed (through some underhanded methods) to his name only. Glory had no knowledge or education about such things, so she accepted it.

Distraught over her circumstances, she moved in with her daughter but continued to see Sam on his terms. But some people, no matter how hard they try, cannot handle the trials of life. Each person has their breaking point. For Glory, it affected her emotionally. She suffered headaches, blackouts, and anxiety attacks, leading to a nervous breakdown. Mentally, she was unable to hold a simple conversation. She only stared into space. The beautiful smile she had, disappeared only to be displayed at times that were inappropriate. She laughed at inappropriate times and often had the most forlorn look on her face and slumped posture. Seeing a person go from 100-10 in her positive attitude was sad. Friends and family members started checking in on her more often. But after a while, the visits became less frequent because people saw no hope or change. It seemed that all hope was lost, and the burden of caregiving was left up to her daughter.

Gradually, with therapy and prayer, she turned her life around, but it took years. The therapist, Ms. May, who worked with Glory, recognized the good heart she had and the potential for her quality of life. Ms. May spent every opportunity to come by the house, having therapy sessions, giving her things to do, praying for her and even taking her out to lunch and church activities. She understood Glory and her circumstances. Although Ms. May had pulled herself up from her troublesome family, she had never seen anything like this. In her family, Ms. May had seen her mother go through similar challenges and commit suicide. She truly felt that Glory was a mission from God and she put her whole heart into saving her because she did not want to see Glory go down the same road. She worked with her individually and gradually got her into group therapy. Eventually, Glory left Sam and started living to help others. Although the process was slow, she became a glowing example of how social and psychological aid can enhance a person's life. Ms. May even managed to help Glory gain employment.

Sam continued to live in the house with his wife. Periodically, he would try to contact Glory to no avail. She had finally gotten him out of her system. She grew in ways that he never expected. Ms. May and Glory became lifelong friends. With Ms. May by her side, she got her GED, started a business selling bakery goods from home, and made enough money to buy her own house. Many of the church members enjoyed her cakes so much that they started a website to help spread the word about her story. She overcame all her trials and was now able to help her daughter and grandchildren. Ms. May also taught her how to manage her money, which helped to straighten out her credit and continue her uphill journey to success. Glory was grateful for Ms. May's support and wanted to find a way to repay her, but Ms. May refused to take anything. She looked at it as part of her job and it gave her comfort to be able to help. Their friendship grew closer and closer and they began to confide in each other, as sisters would do. They were there for each other through the good and the bad times.

Glory continued to work very hard to stay on top of things. This was her way of coping and keeping her head straight. One particular day, after working twelve hours straight, her body gave out. Glory had been experiencing headaches, but she ignored them. She didn't have time to go to the doctor, and insurance was a problem she hadn't had time to straighten out. She got down on her knees, thanking God for all the blessings He had given her. Then she sat down and began to write. When she finished, she got up and called to her daughter in the other room. She walked over to the window and watched the rain as it fell and the beautiful rainbow that had formed across the sky. When her daughter eventually came into the room, she was lying across the bed with that beautiful smile but no more life in her body. She died with notes in her hands to her daughter, Ms. May, Sam, and God. She thanked them for being a part of her life and forgave Sam for all his wrongdoing. Glory now knew that this was the storm she had to go through to reach this point in her life. In the end, she thanked God for always being there for her, putting her in touch with loving and caring people, forgiving her for her sins, helping her get on the right track and for the lessons learned in life to get through it all.

Glory's story is an inspiration to those of us who have to recognize that God is always there but you have to turn it over to Him. He will bring people, things and ideas to you when you least expect it. He knows more about your troubles than you do. When you are ready, He will provide.

Comments:

No human being in this world will ever be exempt from troubles, heartaches or pain. It comes in various ways and at different times. In Glory's story, she had a time of peace in which she was not satisfied. She needed more in her life, felt something important was missing in her life, and that was love. When love comes, it's not always like the fairy tales, neither does it come with a manual. Glory fell hard for a man who didn't feel the same about her. She was willing to share her love with a married man. She trusted him so much that she signed her name on a financial agreement that was not to her benefit. One lesson we must, as women, adults, and parents need to know is that your credit reflects you. Never allow others, boyfriends, husbands, children, friends and other relatives to use your name or money. Unless you have an agreement in writing or a contract, your partner can either leave the debt on you and walk away with no responsibility. In reality, listen intelligently to hear every word and listen with your brain, not your heart. Finally, have faith, believe, pray, listen to what God whispers in your ear for guidance and follow His lead.

The Blinders

We sat together on the bench
But my eyes were affixed.
My husband turned and spoke to me with such
a nasty look.
"What are you looking at?
Do you know that man with the hat?"
He continued with, "You been sleeping with
him."
Is what he shouted out.
In my heart, I knew what this was all about.
He was insecure and controlling with me but
protected the other woman he was seeing.
He had to make sure that my focus was off him
and his cheating.
So, I hung my head down low and looked
straight ahead.
Because the imaginary blinders kept me safe
from everything bad.

"I sought the Lord and He answered me and delivered me from all my fears."

—Psalms 34:4

Silent Abuse - Silent Partner

Silence is not a sign of weakness. Silence is not a sign of being unintelligent. Remember the old saying people used to say, "Watch out for those quiet ones!" those words should be heeded by anyone who may decide to take advantage of the less loquacious people. The quiet one may be a plotter who will catch a person off guard by taking advantage of a situation when it's least expected. They are the ones who will exercise patience and wait for the right moment. The silent one doesn't often allow others to know their true feelings, especially when it comes to being bullied or talked about in a degrading way. The silent one may keep their thoughts and feelings bottled up until one day they explode. The mind can be calculating, analytical, and unpredictable. When the right moment comes, the silent one may attack or simply leave without notice. The target of their vengeance will be left bewildered and unprepared for the change. Betty is a prime example of how the silent one may operate and plan in order to survive.

Joe and Betty have lived together for five years. To the outside world, they looked like the perfect couple. They would go to parties and were always the best-dressed couple. Joe was the life of the party. He would bring Betty in hand and find a place for her to sit. He would always be complimentary, show affection with a kiss, and even say, "I don't know what I would do without her" in public. Betty would sit quietly at these functions. She was always conscious of what she did and how she said things. She would just sit and smile that beautiful smile. Even though Betty was highly educated and an excellent conversationalist, she kept away from that kind of activity for fear of shifty looks from Joe. When asked her opinion, Betty replied with comments that she was sure Joe would agree with. This was one of those times. The party was young and jumping. Betty was sitting quietly when an old male friend started talking and sat next to her. Betty listened attentively then excused herself. She moved to another part of the room.

They left the festivities, where they stayed for only a few hours, seemingly to be the ideal couple. However, the drive home proved to be different. Joe opened the door for his beautiful wife and kissed her on the cheek as their friends watched admirably. He started the car, fastened the seatbelt, and drove down the block. They both sat quietly. Betty reached for the radio to turn on some music. She felt the tension and thought music would ease things. Joe immediately turned it off. Suddenly, Joe tightened the steering wheel, jerked the car to the side of the road, and brought the car to a streaking halt. He started shouting, "See, that's why I hate taking you anywhere. You just sat there looking stupid, as always. You are so embarrassing. Why do you act so dumb? Tell me why? TELL ME WHY!" Betty sat meekly and with fear in her eyes. She started to speak, but before Betty could, Joe interrupted, "Who was that man you were talking to? Forget it! Just shut up. You were right to be quiet because you said some ridiculous things. Next time you can stay at home. I can handle things much better by myself. You just get in the way, and I can't be bothered with watching to see what dumb thing you might say or do next." Just then, a calming spirit came over Joe. "You know, baby, don't worry about a thing. We know you are only good for cleaning up and having babies because you don't do anything else. You just stay cute, and I will take care of everything else." Then Joe pulled Betty close, kissed her on the cheek, and took off again.

Betty was used to this kind of behavior because it was the norm. She tried to please her husband. Once again, she was disappointed by his response, so Betty sat quietly. The pain in her stomach was increasing. In the past, she would defend herself by talking back and even yelling at the top of her lungs. Afterward, she always felt worse because he yelled louder and more aggressively. The worst part of this situation is that Betty loved Joe but hated how he made her feel. In the end, she usually gave in and said she was sorry for the problems she caused without any response from him. Betty now understands that Joe only looks out for her best interest and has accepted her many mistakes. So even though her heart aches, she feels insecure about things, and as a result, Betty has difficulty making decisions around Joe. Therefore, she never disputes anything Joe says.

It took years, but one day as Joe was ranting and raving, Betty tried to reason with him. This time she wasn't as cooperative as she usually was. For weeks Betty has been experiencing problems in her stomach. She has been waking up late at night with acid reflux and vomiting, sometimes coughing up blood. She never said a word to Joe. Betty realized that she usually became ill after she had encounters with him. Betty had made an appointment and had just left the doctor's office. She had been diagnosed with an ulcer and some other stress-related problems. After a brief consultation with her doctor, she was informed that she had two choices to relieve this stress: stop holding on to the bad feeling that stressed her or leave that relationship. Most importantly, the thing that lingered in her mind and her soul was that the doctor said the pain would continue and worsen if things didn't change. He told Betty to take care of herself first and do whatever it took to have a happy life and reminded her happiness was what was best for her and everything else was secondly. That night, Joe came home in a very jovial mood. He talked about his day.

Betty, as usual, had little to say. She hadn't had time to cook because of the doctor's appointment. In addition, Betty had taken a longer route home to reflect on herself. This was the first time she had taken time to search her soul and access her relationship with her husband. She realized the unfortunate turn of events that had been happening to her. It occurred to her that her life was not really her life. It had turned into a daily ritual of catering to Joe's needs. She remembered when they first met and how Joe showed his love for her. Betty remembered the attention, his concern, and charisma that made her fall in love with him. He told her that he loved her and would always care for her, and he had fulfilled that promise. Joe told her that she didn't have to work because that was a man's job to care for his wife. He lived up to this promise. But when all was said and done, she didn't realize that some strings would permanently be attached. It turned out that being taken care of meant that she had to compromise her self-esteem and self-worth, and Joe would finalize all decisions. She had to accept being under the leadership of Joe.

Until now, she made excuses for why she stayed and endured in silence the disrespectful outburst and belittling comments her husband made about her. This time it was different, and Betty felt she had to be selfish to live. When Betty finally got home, she made up her mind to try one more time to talk with Joe about her situation. She wanted to see his reaction before she made any decision. She was in a foggy state of mind and was just about to cook when Joe wanted to know why dinner wasn't ready. She began to explain why but was interrupted. Joe's cheerful attitude turned into a demonic spirit. Joe began yelling for not having his food ready when he got home. He stormed out of the room and told Betty to have his food in an hour. With that, he left the house to who knows where.

In order to get out of a toxic relationship, you have to plan ahead. On Betty's ride home, she had devised: Plan A -to try to talk to him so that they could work on the problems of their relationship. If that didn't work, she knew she had to have a Plan B - to get out. After Joe's explosive behavior with her, Betty decided it was time for the latter. In her heart, she knew her Plan A wouldn't work. On her way home, she had stopped at the bank and withdrawn enough money to get her where she was going and survive. She had filled up her gas tank and stopped to buy a new cell phone. When she got home, Betty packed up enough clothes and put them in the car. She gave herself an hour to complete all the little tasks she had to do to be completely gone before Joe returned. Betty wrote him a lovely note expressing her appreciation and thanked him. She wanted Joe to know that he had taught her a valuable lesson. The lesson was how people could never get something for nothing and that Betty wanted to relinquish his power over her, so she had to leave. She ended the note with hugs and kisses, with an end note - Love Betty. Betty sat his food on the table, with all the settings immaculate. She was walking out of the door with fifteen minutes to spare. She calmly walked to her car and never looked back.

It took her a couple of years to entirely pull herself together. She had her trials, but they seemed to be less strenuous. She appeared to be able to think a little clearer because she was away from Joe's stress. During this interim, Betty discovered God-given talents for business, speaking, decorating, and cooking. Betty used her skills to secure a loan and bought a building. She started Betty's Bakery on the main floor and used the second floor for teaching cooking classes, and business management. Isn't life grand?

Comments:

What is wrong with this scenario? This couple has only one brain to think with, JOE'S. He was the one who was always right and never made any mistakes. He made all of the decisions in the relationship. Betty was made to think she couldn't function without Joe and was incapable of doing anything without his leadership. Ding-ding-ding-ding! Do you hear the bell? That is old-school thinking. Back in the 1700 and 1800s, women were not allowed to do anything without a man's permission. It was her father or brother, but the majority of the time, it was her husband. Even as late as the 1950s, it was hard for a woman to get credit or even buy a house. So generally, women were submissive to men because of financial reasons. The women's rights movement played a critical role in our culture, society, and treatment of women in marriages. Women started to feel that being divorced, an old maid or a widow wasn't taboo. In other words, you could be single, respected and not have to accept the position of being a second-class citizen. Intelligent women went on to further their education and pursue their positions in the workforce, the business world, and the political arena, which was male-dominated until now.

Times have changed! It has been demonstrated throughout the world that women are just as capable of doing anything their hearts desire or that they put their minds to do. Today, it is more about what you are willing to accept into your life and how hard you are willing to work to achieve your heart's desire. A woman's mind is just as receptive to learning and just as capable of doing any job put before her. It should be understood that the mentality "I need a man to take care of me" or "I need a man to take me places" is outdated. For a woman to put herself in this position is putting herself at the mercy of her man.

You can take care of yourself and have a relationship in all kinds of ways. It does not have to be on the level that your partner makes all the rules, and you must abide by them. Relationships are a partnership. God gave you common sense, so use it because no person has all the answers for two. Whether it is about economics or social status, there is nothing that you cannot overcome and make in this world. So many times, I heard young and older women say that their man takes care of them and they can't do it alone. So, they stay in unhealthy relationships. My response is - "Have you tried it yet?" If you do, you will feel much better in the long run without all the negative nonsense always being thrown in their direction. Men who verbally assault women will never stop, no matter how often they are apologetic. This can be the beginning of even more problems to come. Suffering may be physical, mental, or financial, but almost always spiritual. All the Joe's of the world will reap what they sow. Finally, just remember this nobody is perfect. Everyone has faults. (No matter how much they pretend they don't.) Even your abuser. If you have a man like Joe, he uses that simple need to lord over you with derogatory words, constant insults, and instructions on scheduling and how you should act. You don't have to accept any degradation from anyone. A person who cannot treat you respectfully doesn't deserve you. Never let anyone feel they have the right to talk to you in such a way. SPEAK UP FOR YOURSELF! - If all else fails - LEAVE.

What Is Beauty?

Beauty is the smile, the style, and walking that satisfied mile.

Beauty is accomplished, flawless, and not embellished.

Beauty is clean, lean, a sex machine.

Beauty is positive, informative, and collaborative.

Beauty is a love so strong, life-long, with nothing going wrong

Beauty is compatibility, humility, and a place of stability

Beauty is providing a facility and a car with excellent mobility.

As a woman, we look for this in a man

It's the reason a woman wants him to be her number-one fan

But it's unrealistic.

"It is not fancy hair, gold jewelry, or fine clothes that should make you beautiful. No, your beauty should come from inside you; the beauty of a gentle and quiet spirit. That beauty will never disappear and it is worth very much to God."

—I Peter 3:3-4

How Important Is Being a Beauty?

When a woman loves a man, she learns to give a little. When she is privileged to be with him and has little self-confidence, she goes beyond the norm to get or keep the man she wants. In this specific instance, we have a woman named Jill who falls in love with a man named Jack. Jill was not the most attractive woman, but she had a body that many men would fight for. She had a dark complexion and bugging eyes. Her lips were thicker, with the brightest pinkest color and a very noticeable burn on her right cheek. Her hair was long enough to cover up her scar. She usually held her head down, and you could only see half her face. She was about five feet five in the shape of a Barbie Doll. In other words, she was a brick house with the figure 36-24-26. She was known as one of the kindest, sweetest, most giving people you ever wanted to meet. Because she felt unattractive, she concentrated on her books and was an "A-grade" student. As a child, her parents and other family members constantly ridiculed her looks. Jill's father often told her, "I love you, baby, but you had better learn to use your brains because you won't be getting a man by your looks alone."

It was six in the morning, but the sun shone brightly through the light blue and white clouds. Jill was getting ready for school. She enjoyed all of her classes and her teachers, which is expressively demonstrated by her being number one in her class in one of the most prestigious schools in the city. Jill has a sinking feeling of despair when she thinks of her classmates with their negative whispers and looks as she passed them in the school's corridors. Although she was above others academically, she didn't live up to the standards of beauty that America set up in society. She had a body that would knock the socks off of any man, but the color of her dark skin and her facial characteristic was less than desirable. She longed for that one day to find who would stand up for her and love her to the bitter end. The yearning and the need for this special attention and acceptance were hard to come by. Jill never felt secure with her appearance, and it didn't help when others berated her because her nose and lips didn't fit into their prototype of beauty. What happens to a woman who has intellect but not beauty? Where is the love and respect when the man you love only wants to be seen with you in private? Does beauty define a relationship? Finally, is beauty the most important thing to consider in a relationship?

As you read this story about Jack and Jill, consider these questions.

This is why when Jack, with his fine self, wanted to talk to Jill, she had to keep him. On the other hand, Jack was handsome and aware of it. He was told about his handsomeness by everyone since he was born. Jack had what we call a "buff body." He was six feet tall, weighing about one hundred and eighty-five pounds, muscular, and strong enough to be noticed by every woman. His face was like that of an African Prince. He had eyes and a smile perfect enough to light up a room with his presence. Jack had naturally curly hair and beautiful, flawless, clear skin. He was what many a mother dreamed their ideal son would look like. Jack was a fairly level-headed young man who could not take much criticism. He believed in standing by his convictions and fought for the underdog and injustices. He played basketball for his high school team and worked out a lot. His problem was like many of our young people; he worked hard to be a pro basketball player and put little into his class work. This was a crucial time in his life because the school district's new superintendent allowed him a chance to do the necessary work to get passing grades to stay on the team. As the team's star player, he had to find a way to get some help.

Well, it just so happened that he and Jill attended the same school and ran into each other. Jack needed help with his studies, and Jill was available. Suddenly Jill became the target of Jack's charm and good looks to get through school. However, as fate would have it, he fell in love with her but feared what his friends might say. He didn't want his reputation spoiled because he fell in love with an ugly woman. Jack's family added fuel to the fire with comments about him having ugly children and how he would be better off with a more attractive girl. He survived their misguided humor about him and Jill's relationship but never forgot about it. Jack became bitter and confused because he wanted to live with the one he loved, but he didn't like being in public with Jill and defending her to his friends and family. To remedy his fears and insecurities, he started doing things to hide Jill from the public. He wouldn't go anywhere with her. He ignored her whenever they happened to be together in public spaces. Jack would walk the other way for fear of being seen with Jill.

He felt like his mind and heart were torn in half. He loved Jill but not enough to endure the ridicule from his friends and family. He finally stood up for himself; Jack asked Jill to marry him. She accepted his proposal, and they were married. They eloped, and she promised to keep the marriage a secret until the right time to tell everyone. Jack still struggled and continued to feel embarrassed by Jill. The game he was playing was getting to him. Jill felt the pressure whenever he became upset. Jack would blame her for everything that went wrong, claiming she was stopping his social life. He couldn't take the assumption that people were pointing the finger at him and the woman he was with. This continued for ten years.

Jack's class reunion was soon approaching, and the closer it got, the more anxious he became. His friends were talking and asked who he would bring with him. Jack never mentioned that he was married to Jill. They thought that being Jack, he would have the hottest woman in the place. Jill had also heard about the reunion and hoped Jack would invite her. One day while they were having breakfast, Jill mustered up enough courage to ask Jack about it. At that point and time, Jack was fed up with the whole idea and went totally off on her. He expressed himself by saying, "Since when have you ever known me to take you anywhere? I can't be seen with you! What will people think of me if I show up with you on my arm? I just cannot do that." Immediately, he regretted saying those words and walked out of the room.

Jill wanted so badly to be the woman that Jack could be proud of and decided to do something about it. After praying over this problem, one day, Jill's friend advised her to talk to a doctor. Dr. Peterson did facial makeovers and plastic surgery. Oh! There was one crucial fact left out! Due to Jill's superior intellect and excellent business mind, they had become financially well off. Therefore, all the consultations and procedures were no problem. Jack was all for the idea but never said a kind word about the situation. He continued commenting like nothing would ever improve an ugly face like that. With Jack, the dilemma became all about him and how bad this situation made him look and feel.

After months and months of therapy and even surgery, Jill turned out to be more beautiful than anyone ever expected, including Jack. Jack's whole outlook changed now. He wouldn't leave her side. I mean, she couldn't take a breath without him breathing with her. Jill, too, had changed. Jill started feeling better about herself but always remembered who she was. Now things started clicking in her mind telling her that there was nothing wrong with her in the first place. Why did her husband now seem to love her more than before? Wasn't she the same person? Why was he suddenly so attentive and concerned about her? She reminded herself of the things and the actions Jack used to say and do to her, not that she wanted it to happen anymore, but why had the negative comments stopped? Why has his attitude about her attractiveness reversed to praise and possessiveness? This man, who she loved unconditionally, didn't seem to have the same feelings toward her, and it took all of this to make her realize it.

It was so upsetting that Jill decided to leave Jack for a little while to clear her head. Jack couldn't understand her problem. Jill never got over it and never came back. She divorced Jack. She found a man who appreciated her for all she was and had become. He knew and appreciated Jill before and after the reconstruction. From the day he met her in his office, he had always treated her like a queen. You see, the man she married later was Dr. Peterson, who, after their many conversations and consultations, had fallen in love with her even before the surgery.

Comments:

There are several things that can be taken from this story. Before jumping into a serious relationship or marriage, you must value yourself, know who you are, and know what you want from life. Many people don't examine the things they consider important in relationships. They may not have expectations of how it may affect others emotionally and consequences of their self-absorbed actions. They settle for things they know they are not happy with. Some live in such superficial worlds that instead of the examining what is important and their expectations of a relationship, they hide or live with regrets. Obviously, this will lead to an unhappy household. Many are looking through rose-colored glasses and don't see the obvious things until things get serious. If something as apparent as their looks offends a person to the point that they start mentally and verbally abusing you, you need to reexamine your thoughts and reason for being with that person. Women need not accept a relationship that offers them this kind of life. You must always remember never to love anyone more than you love yourself. When you love yourself more, you can look at life with a much clearer picture. A person who loves you and what you are will not hide you from the world. If he loves and respects you, he will parade you out in public proudly at any time and place. Jill finally figured this out after a long time had passed and after all the energy she had put into the relationship with Jack. But that's okay. The time isn't as important. That is a past behavior that can be changed. The result is to truly and ultimately get out of an unhealthy partnership. People don't always make the right decisions. It's like learning to walk. Some babies take a long time to learn, whereas others learn after the first try. The baby may have to fall a few times before getting it. This is the way of life; everyone deals with things differently. Some people get it the first time, while with others, it may take years.

Mother to Daughter

Baby, I love you.
I don't want to see you make a mistake.
God knows I made plenty, and look at where I
am today.
You have such a bright future, don't throw it
away.

Those boys, your friends don't always mean
you well.
In time, you'll see things differently when the
truth is revealed.
Don't let their influence leave you with scars
for a lifetime.
I worry about you because you are mine.

Babies, drug addiction, inability to have long-
lasting relationships,
Physical and mental abuse, rape, and
overbearing friendships.
Although you feel, those things will never
come your way.
This, unfortunately, is what females experience
every day.

As you go through life, remember these things.
Never give up on your dreams.
Never allow people to throw doubt in the stream.
With faith, only God knows how far you can go.
Don't listen to nay-sayers who only make you feel low.
Throughout your struggles, disappointment may come,
Struggles are for a season and can be beaten by determined ones.
Through these struggles, continue to keep the faith.
Life will be better for the ones who can overcome, stay strong and wait.

Again, baby, I love you,
Please listen to the message I'm trying to convey.
You are never too old to learn,
You are never too young to get burned.
No one lives in this world without making mistakes.

The world will persecute you and try to get
you to break.
But the righteous will be courageously
stronger
Because God will bless His survivors to live to
longer.

"The people walking in darkness have seen a great light on the living in the land of the darkness has dawned."

—Isiah 9:2

Decorate My Own Soul and Plant My Own Garden!

Day in and day out, I get in my favorite chair and watch out the window. I don't have anything to do. My husband said I needed to do something. I told him that's what I have you for. He worked hard every day and faithfully bought home his check to me. He bought me this chair right before he died of a heart attack at work. So, I sit in this chair in his memory. I have to smile because he told me to get a job, and then he kills himself working. Today, my job is to watch everybody on the block break their necks to get to work. I got enough money to get me by. I just got to find another man to look out for my best interest. I get up early in the morning and sit in my recliner chair in order to get to my job and check for potential prospects to sponsor me. I brush my teeth, comb my hair, put on a clean top, and smile at everyone who passes by. I love it! I laugh because I can't do that. That's another whole story in itself. I'm allergic to work. Most people are friendly, but that neighbor of mine is something else. For some reason, we have a mutual dislike for each other. That's because she knows I will take her hard-working, good-looking man and show her how ungrateful of a wife she is.

I see her every day. I just look out the window and watch her as she walks past. She strolls in a slow stride, and with every step, her head is high in the air. Who does she think she is anyway? She ain't no better than nobody else.

She thinks she's cute and better than everybody else. I can't stand her. A few years ago, she was with that crazy man, walking with her head almost dragging on the ground. She didn't think she was so cute then. She didn't even have a job or decent clothes. Then she called herself going to school or something. It doesn't matter, though, because I have always had a man to care for me. I look better, and what she is doing is stupid. Sometimes she had all the kids with her, and they all walked around with their heads down because that man was getting them going and coming. He had strict rules in his house. You could hear him all the way down the street. "If you live in my house where I pay the bills and take care of you, you gonna do what I say!" He decorated everything about him, head to toe, and even the car he drove. He dressed finer than fine or, as they say, finer than wine. He took care of all the bills at home, but out of every check, he bought something for himself. This left little money, if anything, to give to his wife and children. I remember she came over to confide in me about her concerns. She said it was too much for her and wanted to leave. I told her straight up, "You better keep that man. If you don't want him, send him to me." She stayed with him, but she stayed in school too. She answered me with, "One day, I'm leaving. As soon as I can, I'm leaving. I can have more peace and satisfaction taking care of myself." I wanted to tell her so badly to let that man take care of her and do what he said so she won't have to go to work. That was her last visit with me.

Now I look at her. I mean, seeing her prance down the street burns me up like that. You know she finished school. I watch her. Little by little, her head started to rise while walking down the street with him. I also noticed that now instead of just hearing his voice during their weekly arguments, I listen to her too. Nowadays, he leaves the house more often and stays out for long periods, but he always comes home. I knew something was wrong, but I couldn't quite grasp it. I knew he was bound to be leaving soon.

One day I decided to exercise my curiosity and allow my reputation to do a little investigation. As he walked past my house, I called to him and invited him over. We had a great time. We laughed a little, talked a little, and even spent a little time upstairs (if you know what I mean). I was very, very satisfied when he left. He came by a couple more times, then he suddenly stopped. After that, he simply ignored me. This particular day, while I sat on the porch, I made it my business to inquire as he walked by. He just laughed and kept going.

About a year later, they both left the house in the morning at the same time together, but they went in different directions. I wanted to say something to them but just watched through the curtains. It seemed like she was acting a little uppity, and I just didn't want to be bothered with her at all. I don't know if word got around that he had been by for those visits or if he had told her. All I noticed was that she had nothing to say to me. Another thing that I noticed was that she was dressing better these days. She got herself a job and was now wearing designer this and designer that from head to toe. She out-dressed him.

But in my gut, I still felt she had made a mistake. I wanted to tell her how much of a fool she was and crazy for not allowing this man to be a man. He literally was doing what a man is supposed to do. She could have worked her charm on him, got him to do whatever she wanted him to, and not have to work a lick. Just let me get a hard-working, good-looking man who pays my bills. Forget whatever problems I have with him. I'm staying home and doing everything he wants me to do. But not her. Huh! She went and got a job. She considered herself to be better than other people.

His attitude seemed to be changing too. His behavior was not as transparent, but I did notice the difference. He wouldn't talk to me anymore, and he became more docile and quieter. I don't know why, but I didn't hear yelling anymore.

But seriously, I don't care anymore. They both deserve each other. I think there's something wrong with both of them. We haven't really had many conversations since I gave her that sound advice. So, what if she heard rumors about him coming by? She still had him. And him! He doesn't know what a good catch he had with me! I would have catered to his every need. All he had to do was go to work and bring the money in.

As time passed by, my neighbor became more and more independent of each other. I heard from the girl down the street that she had gotten a promotion on her job. She also had the nerve to return to school for more education. How ridiculous is that! That is out and out stupid! What does she need to go back to school for? People like her are just wasting their time and money. Look at me! I graduated from high school and didn't want or need any more schooling. They can't teach me nothing, and they ain't gon help me get a job. However, I must admit from my sources that she is making more money than him. I believe it too. I see how it affects their relationship because I saw him putting his stuff in a truck and leaving the other day. I overheard him yell his insecurities back at her that she didn't need him because she was making enough to care for herself. And girl, you know, she didn't seem the least bit upset. She walks down the street with a smile, sashaying as she walks like she doesn't have a care in the world. She looks so peaceful and happy. She walks now with her head held high in the air and seems to be so proud.

One day I saw her and simply couldn't take it anymore. I had to ask her why. I wanted to know how she had made such a drastic change with so many different things in her life. Believe me, I didn't want to, but it was eating me up. I had to find out why a person like her is so happy when obviously so much was going wrong. So, I called her. She stopped. I told her how I felt and asked her straight out. What was wrong with her? She looked at me with a smile. She didn't seem the least angry with me and answered politely, "The things you feel are important. I don't. My mother has always told me to plant my own garden and decorate my own soul. She told me it would take time and that you may have trouble along the way, but never give up because the sun will shine brighter in the end." She started to walk away, then turned around and said, "My mother said that if God has a plan for you and you believe in it, he will show you the way. So don't worry. Although I suffered, I'm glad I went back to school and got a job. I'm glad for the things I have experienced because they taught me what I don't want in my life. Now I can take care of myself and my children. I have planted my own garden and have decorated my own soul with the things that have done nothing but make me feel good about myself. Now, I proudly say that I wouldn't want to feel any other way!" With those words said, she quickly turned and walked away like she was all that.

I never bothered her anymore. After a couple of years passed, I couldn't. She moved to another neighborhood, a better one. She and her kids were now well off because she managed to get a lot of money off an investment tip in toilet paper and other business ventures. She started her own business, which appears to be doing very well. I never saw her husband again, but I did hear about him. He was staying across town with another woman paying all her bills, still buying new clothes, and preaching about he pays the bills, so she has to do as he says.

Comments:

As a child, coming up in a family of ten, my parents taught all her children - boys and girls - to cook, budget money, clean up iron-and not to wait on anyone to take care of them. They pushed this lesson to emphasize never relying on others because it will give them the power to lord over. They wanted us to learn much for ourselves to be independent, successful, responsible, and strong. Education and finding a skill to prepare you for an abundant future was their way out for us. This was their way of telling us to plant our own garden. We learned to decorate our own souls with success and higher self-esteem because of it.

Verbal abuse is something that many people tolerate because they feel that it is not that bad; they are not always like this; he loves me. He was just having a bad day; he didn't mean it. He loves me, and who else I'm going to rely on; or, "What have I done to make this happen?" In addition, verbal abuse can be a contributor to financial abuse. The worst line is, "You are going to do what I say because I take care of you," as if you have to maintain your submission position in the partnership. You must realize that relationships are made of two human beings with different personalities. You have to get to know your mate before you make commitments. Certain signs are obvious, but you often ignore them because you are looking through dream world. You only see how attractive he is. You only know how he dresses, the car, and the money he gives you. You only hear the flattering words he uses to reel you in. Later you find out that he has this alternate ego that starts to be extremely controlling through his belittling words and his habit of monitoring every penny you make and spend. How many times have you been told he does this because his mother was treated this way? Be aware of his problems with his ex, and now he can't see his kids or his basic opinion of the role of women. Worst of all, he tells you that he is the man of the house, and you must do as he says. You miss their philosophy of what gender roles are in a relationship. Many times, these can be discovered in conversation, which today, so many of us miss because of lust, being misinformed or lied to, not listening carefully enough, and not being focused on the things you need to know.

The signs to look for are:

1. Does your mate value and respect your opinion?
2. Is there respect in the way that he speaks and treats you?
3. Are you on an equal basis in the decision-making of the partnership?
4. Are you in a relationship that allows both of you to grow to your fullest potential or as far as you want to with a mutual understanding?

If any of these answers are no, you may want to consider whether you want to spend more time with this person. In addition, the older women will tell you the way you go into a relationship is the way it will be. They don't change. This is where relationships fail because we don't focus on the things that are needed to have long-lasting successful relationship compatibility and mutual respect. Finally, don't start off traveling through the darkness; pay attention and look for the signs, and you will see that the light as it dawns.

God's Time

God's time is not the same as your time
Even though we get weary, complain, and
whine,
God knows how much you can bear.
Although troubles may come, and you think
He doesn't care.
Remember, it's God's plan and His time that
bought you here.

God's time is not the same as your time.
Difficulties may seem to linger on.
You ask the questions, "When do I get to pass
the baton?"
Remember, there are lessons to be learned here
He is waiting for you to get there.

God's time is not the same as your time.
He works in mysterious ways.
Sometimes people transition suddenly and just
go away.
While others who exhibit no quality of life may
hang on by a thread, and their life just lingers
on.

Remember, He knows the day, the time, and your song.

What does this all boil down to?
We can't decide when to quit.
We can only ask and submit.
He has the final word about what he will permit.
Remember, He has the final word about what he will permit.

"Rise up; this matter is in your hands. We will support you so take courage and do it."

—*Ezra 10:4*

Miss Nettie' Porch

It came like a dream at three o'clock in the morning. Lying in bed alone, in pitch dark, with complete silence, her mind wandered. This was a ritual that seemed to happen every night. However, this night felt different. Just about the time sleep began to pull her into la-la land, a bright light appeared to be walking into the room. Nettie's first thought was to run. But where? Also, with Nettie's old legs, she wouldn't make it. The light was blinding. She now put her hands over her eyes so that she could see and shield them. The light hands were reaching out to me, and a strange feeling came over her as she got close to the bed. Then just as quickly as it appeared, it disappeared. Nettie knew then it was time to rise, with God's lead, and to lend a helping hand to those women who needed her help. Now knowing the task before her, she prepared her mind, body, and soul and announced to herself, "Nettie, get ready! They will be coming."

Ms. Nettie, was that nosy neighbor on the block? This woman got up early in the morning, sat on her porch, or peeked out of the window seven days a week, rain or shine, only to move when she had to go to the bathroom or get something to eat. Her porch was the community's parking lot for advice, gossip, rumors, lies, protection, and just good times. Believe it or not, Ms. Nettie has an important job in the community. She was similar to Griots in the ancient African villages. In our neighborhood, if you ever wanted to know anything about the community, especially to get a helping hand, the place to go in our neighborhood was Miss Nettie's Porch.

Miss Nettie was a feisty older lady who always had at least ten cats and two dogs. When you passed by her house, she was either on her front or back porch. Middleweight, short, and dark-skinned, she could be very friendly or mean-spirited. It would depend on how her day was going or what side of the bed she got up on. With so many animals in her yard, cats walking along her tall fence, or the dogs constantly barking, children would come along and intimidate them many times. With Miss Nettie, if you mess with her animals, you mess with her. So, she would sit on the back porch to watch them. Whenever children bothered the animals, Miss Nettie was prepared with her machete to threaten them and a few choice words to keep them at a distance. As she sat quietly on her back porch, she would often observe the children going to and coming from school. She found ways to chastise them with a word to them or their parents.

Because of her relationship with so many neighbors, she was well respected and had no problem using her leverage to get people on the straight and narrow. With Ms. Nettie, you mess with her friends and neighbors you mess with her. Miss Nettie's front porch was used for entertainment. Young and old people would come by and sit on her porch to watch the drama that happened in full view. No matter how horrible the situation was, there was always some humor and some positive lesson in the happenings. Sometimes, the elders would turn these times into counseling sessions. She fully believed in a village raising a child and neighbors helping one another. This was where many of the young women in the neighborhood came when they were experiencing problems in a relationship. Miss Nettie, who was well-equipped to advise on her life journey, would provide guidance and even help save a life or two. She had an excellent listening ear and had a down-to-earth way of getting her point across. She understood that what people needed was someone to be in their corner when they needed it.

One case especially sticks out in my mind. It happened in the winter of 1985. Ms. Nettie looked out the window and saw the drama unfolding. She saw a young lady named Red running down the street and her husband chasing her. He was grabbing at her clothes while cussing her out and reminding her that she was his wife. When he finally caught up to her, he knocked her to the ground and dragged her through the snow to a place he thought no one would see them. He commenced beating her even further. Ms. Nettie came out on her porch with her gown on and started yelling down the street, "Leave that girl alone before I come out with my gun! I have already called the police, and they are coming. Now get your ass away from that girl." He hesitated for a minute and then hollered back, "Old lady, you better mind your own business before I come over there and beat your motherfucking ass!" Ms. Nettie yelled back, "Bring it on," then pulled the gun from behind her back and pointed at him. The young lady was slowly trying to get away from her husband. Ms. Nettie saw the fear in her eyes and got angry. "Red, get your ass up before I shoot you for being stupid. Come on in this house NOW!" She knew what to expect since this was not the first exchange she had experienced. The police drove up just in time to catch the young man attempting to escape. Ms. Nettie placed the gun back in her pocket. Red's husband knew he was in trouble because the police had warned him about his behavior, and he knew of the reputation of Ms. Nettie in the community. The police respected her. He knew they would listen to her before they listened to him. Red pulled herself away slowly and ran up to Ms. Nettie's porch. Through Ms. Nettie's counseling, praying, and a good cussing out, the young lady managed to break away from her husband.

It took time, and Red didn't stop right after that time. She went back time after time. Ms. Nettie was always there for her, giving her a listening ear and sound advice. Ms. Nettie would say, "Okay, what happened this time? You know if you stay, it will only get worse! So, you had enough yet?" She went through having a gun pulled on her in front of her son while threatening to kill her in front of him. Again, Ms. Nettie would say, "Okay, what happened this time? You know if you stay, it will only get worse. So, you had enough yet?" Red went through him getting married to another woman while still being married to her, and the worst part about it was that she was in the hospital having his second child. Finally, it stuck with Red with Ms. Nettie saying, "Okay what happened this time? You know if you stay, it will only get worse. So, you had enough yet?" But the final straw was when she announced that she was getting a divorce. He came by her house, threw a computer at her, and broke her jaw. Through the healing process, she finally realized that this was not the life she wanted for herself or her children. Red thought of the appreciation for Ms. Nettie and how these things happened each time; Ms. Nettie was always there for her with sound advice. Throughout the many years of abuse and the different ordeals, Red appreciated the patience, the time, and the method Ms. Nettie took with her to help get her out of such a negative situation. Most of all, Ms. Nettie never judged her. She now decided she would do what she could to help others. She now understood that no matter how good or bad you think life is, you should be thankful for life when you wake up each day. She knew now that there was someone somewhere out there fighting for survival like she was. She decided to give back like Ms. Nettie had been doing.

On another occasion, Ms. Marie, the next-door neighbor, came over and sat on the porch with Ms. Nettie and Red. They all sat there quietly that night because it was a nice breeze and a beautiful full moon. They all sat there looking at the stars and the moon when Ms. Marie broke the silence with, "I just wish he would move." No one else said a word. They just let her talk. She continued, "He comes in every payday starting fights just so he can go out. Then he spends all the money on that other woman. That leaves me all the responsibility of taking care of the house and the six kids. But tonight, I have had it. Lately, he has begun to mistreat the children more and more. Little Frank is seriously showing signs of distress and has been increasingly peeing in the bed. I had been hiding it from Big Frank, but he found out before he left today. He called Little Frank to the room and made him suck the urine off the sheets. I don't know what I'm going to do." There was complete silence for a while. Everyone continued to watch the skies. Then Ms. Marie broke down crying and fell to her knees. The other two women reached out to her and began to hug her. Consoling was the only thing they could do because there was a complete loss for words.

Finally, after some time, the three women devise a plan to get rid of Big Frank. Operation Ousting Big Frank was in the process. The first step was to get someone into his confidence and record some of his conversations about his exploits. Ms. Nettie glared at her and wondered if she would follow through this time. She really hesitated with Ms. Marie because there had been times when she offered to help, offered her advice, and was told to mind her own business. But this time, Ms. Nettie felt something was different. Also, she had heard that Big Frank was planning to leave anyway. So, at this point, she felt that Ms. Marie would need a boost of confidence to get through this dilemma. Ms. Nettie took a deep breath, lifted Ms. Marie's head, and said, "This time, you had better make sure this is what you want because there is no turning back because my God is getting ready to get him out of that house. You hear me! There is no turning back. It's in God's hands. You hear me! It's in God's hands." Ms. Nettie gave Ms. Marie a journal and told her to write down everything he did whenever he left the house. She told her that the journal would help her focus more and encourage her. Ms. Nettie told

122

her to trust herself because she knows more than she thinks she does.

Ms. Marie, Red, and Ms. Nettie understood that in order to get out of an abusive relationship, you have to be on top of everything. You have set up an ironclad plan.

Step one of any escape plan is to always get the support of God. Led by Ms. Nettie, the three women meditated and began to pray:

"Dear God,

Please hear my voice. You know our situation and the troubles Ms. Marie has in her house. Please touch her and her children. Keep your angels around them and give them the protection and the strength they need to Get That Man Out of Her House! Help us to help you wherever it is needed. Provide her with the financial blessings to keep her and her children fed, clothed, and sheltered. Give them the emotional and spiritual support they need to survive without Big Frank! Finally, dear God, let it be that one day, one day-Big Frank will realize the error of his ways, confess his sins to you and move completely out. In

the name of the Father, Son, and the Holy Spirit!
AMEN!"

Step two of the plan was on Ms. Marie and her faith in God. Ms. Nettie gave her a few scriptures of the bible and told her to read these scriptures every day between noon and twelve-thirty, followed by a prayer, in order to give her the focus and strength to complete this task. Ms. Marie instructed her that once God steps in, miraculous things will happen. Ms. Nettie and Red went over to Ms. Marie's house, cleaned it from top to bottom, and prayed over everything because God appreciates a clean environment. This also cleans out all the impurities, clears the mind, and makes the house look more presentable. With all this going on, the women, especially Ms. Marie, felt they could conquer the world. But the most challenging part was yet to come. Ms. Nettie advised Ms. Marie that if you give people time and space; if you don't beg them to stay; if you just let them roam, you will find that what's meant for you will always be yours.

The third step of their plan was to go through as many of Franks' financial records, his bank records, insurance papers, and any receipts around the house to find out where his money was going and how much he had. This was a tedious and time-consuming job but essential because Big Frank managed all the money, and Ms. Marie never had the opportunity to see a dime. She would ramble through his stacks and stacks of papers and bills. She found insurance papers, receipts, and pictures of him and another lady friend out partying. Ms. Marie devised a folder with all the information she found to free herself. She took this folder and locked it up in a special box that Ms. Nettie had under her porch with the dogs. Also, because she didn't work (because he didn't want her to work), they had to devise a plan for her to become more financially independent. She had to find a way to convince Big Frank that it would be in his best interest for her to get a job. These things, most importantly, devised an avenue for her to get the divorce with child support and maybe even spousal support. This little progress would eventually add up to the big result of ending this relationship.

The prayers and blind continuous work on her plan gave her the courage to successfully get Big Frank out of her life. She now had a job that Red had set her up for with an agency she worked for, and Big Frank was happy about the extra money coming into the house. Red helped her prepare for the interview; told her what to expect, and even communicated with the people she knew would hire her. In addition, Big Frank's job as a janitor allowed them to live rent-free. God worked it out that she now made more money than he did. He noticed a little change in her behavior but didn't let that bother him. He had a better relationship now with his new woman, and she required more and more. He didn't care because the more he gave her, the more she treated him like a king. God had it all worked out. Ms. Marie now felt more empowered and happier. Her children were happier because their dad was home less and less. God had it all worked out. In all ways, they were already separated, just as God planned and all parties involved seemed content.

Finally, the day came when Big Frank announced that he was leaving to be with the love of his life. He said he was not staying in a relationship that did not benefit him. He said he wanted to live his life without being tied down by a wife and kids. He felt that now since Ms. Marie had a job and was doing so well, she would accept everything as is and that he could walk away. Big Frank seriously thought Ms. Marie was too afraid to say anything to him and that she didn't have the courage or sense to do anything to change his plans. But according to the plan by Ms. Nettie and her girls, this was exactly how they wanted him to think. Ms. Marie was told to be cooperative and act in a way that would not make him suspicious. They had already set up the best way and the best time to proceed to the next step with a lawyer. God allowed Big Frank to think that he was going to greener pastures and that living away from all the drama he felt he had with Ms. Marie was okay. But we must remember that selfishness and arrogance will always come back and bite you in the butt. God allowed Ms. Marie and her children a way, the strength, and the mindset to get out of the drama Big Frank brought into their household.

Needless to say, Big Frank was surprised when the divorce papers arrived at his new house. Ms. Marie didn't know exactly what day he would receive them. But when he received them, she knew immediately because Big Frank came to her as she sat on Ms. Nettie's porch. With tears in his eyes, he wanted to know why she had made such a move. In his eyes, he had not done anything to hurt her. He pleaded with her to understand that she was the love of his life. He pleaded with her to let him return and promised he had changed. He explained that he was unhappy where he was now and had seen the error of his ways. But honestly, Big Frank saw that she was asking for child and spousal support. A deep-seated fear had come over him. He knew that he would not be able to afford to keep his new life, pay for the support of his wife, pay child support for four children, and pay for health insurance. The only thing Ms. Marie could say to him was we had all these kids together, and you will help support them. Even if that means you are broke! Goodbye! As she sat there watching him as he walked away, the words of Ms. Nettie came back to when she said, "This time you had better make sure this is what you want, because there is no turning back because my God is getting ready to get him out of that house. You hear me! There is no turning back! It's in God's hands! You hear me! It's in God's hands!" she couldn't turn back, and she couldn't hear a word he was saying. There was also the time and energy that Ms. Nettie and Red put into helping her achieve her goal of escaping a sad situation for her and her children. Finally, she had to admit that she and her children felt much better without an arrogant, selfish and uncaring man in the house who was constantly belittling, terrorizing, and abusing them at every opportunity he could. It felt like a weight had been lifted off her shoulders and that she could now stand up straight and be proud. She was out of the cocoon Big Frank had put her and her children in. She now had the energy and the vision to see all the opportunities the world had to offer them.

As the years went by, Big Frank married and divorced several women. He could never find another Ms. Marie. The children, although they suffered from some of the scars of their childhood, basically followed in their mother's footsteps. She never criticized their father and allowed them to make their own decisions about him. However, the relationship between

Big Frank and his children is strenuous because he never was a giving or loving father. He was only around for special occasions or in times of illness, but their mother was always there. One day Big Frank suffered a massive stroke and became paralyzed on one side of his body. He was unable to work or even take care of all those little things that he took for granted. He needed help with daily activities like getting from here to there because he had lost the ability to walk. Although he could move in a wheelchair, once he got into it, he had to get dressed and get into the chair to go anywhere. He had to learn to use his left hand because his right side was paralyzed. But, being the man he was, he never completely changed. Even though he left scars on Ms. Marie and the children, he still needed to be the controlling and abusive person he had always been. The children felt bad for him but could not and did not want to care for him. He had been so ornery and neglectful toward them in the past, and even in the condition after the stroke, his behavior was inconsistent. At first, he was glad to see them, but eventually, his true self came out. A person's personality doesn't change just because they experience an illness. The children realized that the best solution was to transfer their 65-year-old father to a nursing home.

The nursing home did what it could, but many things were neglected. The problem was that the staff wasn't as nurturing to him as they could have been because of his attitude. In addition, because no family members visited, the staff mistreated and neglected him. He was lonely and still never understood why him! He worried so much that he wound up having another stroke and died there alone. Before the stroke, he had written a letter saying he was sorry for whatever he had done to deserve his family's mistreatment. The only thing he wanted from them was their forgiveness and that they would give him a decent burial. Finally, he said this would probably be the last time they would hear from him. He expressed that he wished things had turned out differently and that he still loved them.

Ms. Nettie, Red, Ms. Marie, and her children were the only ones who attended the funeral. It was a sad occasion, but it was like the closing of bad times never to come again. They all sat with a sigh of relief. The repast was arranged to be on Ms. Nettie's Porch. The family reminisced, ate, and finally left Ms. Nettie, Red, and Ms. Marie. The three of them sat quietly. The silence broke when Ms. Nettie said, "Be prepared and look out for others to come to us."

Comments:

Some sections of society work together to always look out for their own kind. The most dominant one is the male species. Some are more liberal than others, but societies all over the world have been dominant in male control. Men work together to keep it that way. Sure, women have made many achievements over the year, but as of today, we do not have females in complete control of any society. The group that controls and decides the rules of the world. Women will continue to be the underdog because men make the rules. Women must learn to look out for one another and simply lend a helping hand whenever it's needed. This is an important way to empower the women of the world.

A Friend in Deed

Loyal, trustworthy, honest, and keeping it real,
That's a true friend
Helpful, empathic, and understanding
How you feel,
That's a true friend.

Confidant, inspiring, inclusive, and motivating
That's a true friend.
Responsible, respectful, reliable, and
accommodating
That's a true friend.

Friends may come, and friends may go.
Because the forks in the road may take you
separate ways
Friends may not always be with you when
you're low
Life's choices, disagreements, and paths may
separate you for years, weeks, or days.

But as time passes, in that unspecified moment,
their paths cross

With no blame or shame, but an
understanding, caring heart, and a listening ear
Their friendship continues as if there is no time
to lose.
That is a true friend indeed, my dear!

"Do nothing out of selfish or vain conceit. Rather, in humility, value others above yourselves."
—Philippians 2:3

Never Say Never

Maggie was a college student who always kept her goals ahead of her. Her goals were to be a doctor someday and start her own clinic in order to give back to the community. Maggie was always at the top of her class. However, her arrogant attitude about life, herself, and other people's problems left her lonely. She had no filter when telling people the right thing to do and what she wouldn't do. In addition, she had a very nonchalant attitude that made it impossible for her to care about anything. Regarding her relationships, she was very controlling and never let her emotions rule her. Therefore, she felt that all mistakes and breakups in her relationships were due to the other person.

Maggie has been my friend since grade school. We used to share everything together. She was a kind, intelligent, and beautiful child of God. She was the child many parents wished for because of her responsible nature and never caused a bit of trouble. No one ever complained about Maggie. Of course, she had her faults because she tried very hard to be a perfectionist, which sometimes bothered her family. Also, she was quick to tell others of their faults. She had some friends but not many because most people could not deal with her brutal honesty. By the time Maggie completed high school, she had one good friend, Virginia. Virginia was the one friend she could talk to about anything because she was a quiet person and a good listener. This was the key to their excellent relationship because Maggie only wanted to be listened to. She always had the answers and had little empathy for others. Maggie was known for saying, "Oh that would never happen to me."

As life would have it, Virginia and Maggie started to drift apart. Their season as friends changed when Virginia began a relationship with a man in their neighborhood named Charlie. Charlie was the first guy to give her attention and made her feel good about herself as a woman. The one thing he required of her was that she only be with him all of the time. In the beginning, Virginia's heart let her believe that this man was all she needed, and she wanted to do everything to keep him. This meant cutting all ties with Maggie except for an occasional phone call.

Everything was fine. Charlie and Virginia were inseparable. Charlie doted over Virginia every minute of the day. They discovered they had so much in common that they decided to marry. They were into each other, willing to experiment with new adventures together. Then, Charlie decided to move them away from their hometown. This made them more committed to one another and inseparable. Charlie's needs always came first, and all the experiments were really a way to gain full control of the relationship. Everything was perfectly fine with Charlie as long as Virginia followed his lead. It never occurred to him that she had any opinion about anything. Afterall, he grew up in a household where his father treated his mother the same way. He knew what was best for them at all times. With this being Virginia's first relationship, she thought this was how a relationship should go. She never thought of the outcome of what could happen if one person had full control of all decisions. It became difficult for Virginia when he separated Virginia from her friends and family. He bought her gifts and treasured her but refused to let her go outside for anything. The gradual domination of Virginia's life caused her to drift into a state of loneliness and depression. Charlie felt she should be grateful and never wanted to hear any of her complaints. She had to pretend that all was well whenever he was around or deal with his fury. His fury could range from smothering her with love, expressing remorse and sorrow while trying to convince her to think that it was all being done for them, to her being told that she should be grateful to have a man like him. It could go as far as him slapping her for being ungrateful and locking her up in a room with locked windows until she recognized the error of her ways.

After years of unhappiness, the time came when Virginia could no longer take it. Her mind now was so distraught from the routines of the day that she tended to move around the house like a robot. She was trying to get dinner ready before he got home, but mentally she was struggling. She couldn't take ten steps without having to sit down. Time was running short before Charlie was to be home, so she put the food in the oven and bathed. Before she stepped into the tub, she took a handful of pills to relax. Virginia got into a comfortable sleep as she laid her back in the comfort of the warm water. She stayed there long enough for the food in the oven to burn, which ultimately caused the house to catch fire. Virginia woke up to smoke.

She dragged herself out of the tub and grabbed her robe and house shoes just in time to save herself. Neighbors gathered around the house, not knowing that Virginia even lived there because no one ever saw her. Virginia was groggy, and she sat on the sidewalk and watched the house go up into flames.

Nevertheless, neighbors comforted her until the police and firemen came. They put the fire out before it completely destroyed the house. Charlie pulled up just before the paramedics put Virginia into the ambulance. He insisted that he see his wife and tried to stop them from taking her away, but it was Virginia's request for him not to come. Charlie knew in the back of his mind that this would be the last time he would see Virginia, and he was right.

Virginia stayed in the hospital because the medical professionals considered her a suicide risk. Charlie used every tactic to get Virginia back home. He even went so far as to refuse to pay the hospital bill. When Virginia heard about this, she said that was the last straw. She spoke with her therapist and later to the authorities about the conditions in her household. They helped her to get a lawyer who immediately asked for an order of protection which led to her filing for divorce. Charlie was banned from the hospital and just in case he managed to get in, a policeman was found sitting outside the room for a few days. With therapy and a sudden sense of freedom, Virginia concluded that no one would run her life but her ever again. She realized that she could've died and no one would have ever known because they hadn't seen her. Most of all, she understood that Charlie was more in love with his control and dominance over her than her as a person. When Virginia made this decision, she felt free as a bird and that no man would get in her way again. She made up her mind to start a whole new life away from Charlie by moving to another town and getting a job in a hospital. She bought herself a dog for the company to satisfy her loneliness and to take time away from relationships for a while. She found a job where she worked with the social service department in a hospital and joined a church in the area.

The town Virginia moved to just so happened to be the same place that Maggie was living. Virginia wanted badly to get in touch with Maggie with all that had happened, but she wasn't comfortable enough to try. Virginia also felt a little inferior to an old friend who had progressed so far beyond her in life. She eventually put it in her mind that if it was God's will, one day, it would happen. Maggie had seen Virginia around and had heard from her family about the problems she had gone through. She was distraught with Virginia for putting herself in that situation and considered her weak and unworthy of her friendship. Maggie made it her business to stay as far away from Virginia as possible. Up to this time, Maggie had not experienced any of the life lessons Virginia had faced. She felt invincible, and her arrogance made her feel above all that nonsense. But God does not discriminate. In His eyes, everyone will experience some ups and downs. It is the only way we learn to appreciate the good times and learn to do better is from our lessons. Virginia had her experience, and now Maggie was about to learn her lesson.

It all started while Maggie was in medical school. On that unforgettable day, Maggie met Dr. Right. She thought she had the man of her dreams. He was the Chief of Cardiology at Mercy Hospital and had the mind, body, spirit, and drive she had always looked for in a man. He looked like a god from his face to his well-built body. When he spoke to her at the hospital that day, she felt like a cube of ice melting into the floor. As you can tell, Maggie fell in love with Dr. Right as soon as she saw him. She found every opportunity to be near him. She even changed her specialization from pediatrics to cardiology so she could work under Dr. Right. If she found out about a meeting he had to attend, Maggie attended too. She knew where his favorite restaurants were, his days off, and his hobbies. Whenever Maggie could be near him, she did; in classes or meetings, she always had a question just to show Dr. Right how much she knew and so she could be noticed. It wasn't long before Dr. Right started looking forward to seeing her. He admired her aggressiveness and the attention she gave him. Finally, Dr. Right asked Maggie out to dinner. They continued to date but not in the open. Dr. Right was Maggie's superior at the hospital, and it would not look good for such a relationship to happen in this situation. In addition, Dr. Right was still married, and he informed Maggie that he was waiting for the right time to divorce his wife. For two years, Maggie was Dr. Right's secret lover, and this was perfect in Maggie's world. She was not interested in anyone else as she was with the man of her dreams.

But as life would have it, things change. It was after class one night when Maggie decided to stick around and wait for the dinner date with Dr. Right. After all, it didn't make sense to go all the way across town and have to come back in an hour. Maggie wanted to ensure she wasn't late because she had something serious to talk to him about. She waited for him to come to their usual meeting place. Dr. Right was always prompt, so she knew she had little time to kill.

The room was beginning to get cool, so Maggie walked down to the canteen area to get a cup of coffee. Sitting in the canteen was Jeff, a young man in her class, who was always watching her. Maggie never trusted him because he always stared like he was undressing her. She walked in and went straight to the coffee machine. When she turned around, she saw Dr. Right sitting across the room, talking to a charming and fashionably dressed young lady. They seemed to be having more of a friendly talk than something that coworkers would have. To Maggie, the conversation appeared to be too cozy and too personal. This woman was not someone she had seen working in the hospital. The woman's appearance was too flirting to be about business or friendship. Her legs were crossed seductively, showing more of her thighs than needed. She leaned her body ever so slightly toward Dr. Right, just enough for him to notice her breast. When she glanced over to Dr. Right, he had a permanent smile as he soaked in every bit of the flirting. They were totally engrossed with each other that they didn't notice Maggie while she was in the room. Maggie got her coffee and left without saying a word.

Maggie was upset over the matter but didn't know what to do. She was only a few months away from graduation, and now this happens. At that point, Maggie couldn't say anything because she was hurt and afraid Dr. Right might leave her. She also didn't want to jump to the wrong conclusion. As the hurt grew, the tears fell because she thought Dr. Right was her husband-to-be. After all, he had just promised last week that his divorce would be finalized by the time Maggie graduated and that they would get married. She wiped her tears and pondered over the whole dilemma. Although she couldn't pull herself all the way together, she made up her mind to just drop it, sit, and wait for her date to come at the appointed time.

Jeff happened to be passing by and noticed the sad, forlorn look on Maggie's face. He asked her if he could help in any way. Maggie didn't want to confide in him about her thoughts, so she pretended everything was okay. In her heart, she wanted to tell him or anybody. At this point, and how Maggie felt, she wanted to scream to the world but couldn't. Besides, it was almost time for Dr. Right to come, and he was always on time. When Dr. Right arrived, he didn't mention anything about the other woman, and neither did Maggie.

Months went by, and Maggie graduated with high honors. Dr. Right told her they would have to wait to get married because the divorce had not gone as smoothly as he thought it would. They continued to see each other secretly because Dr. Right said he didn't want to give his wife any ammunition to use against him in court. Maggie got a job in the hospital near him and later started her practice in the neighborhood she had grown up in. Everything was going fine with her life. She had the man of her dreams and was financially stable. She had a practice that was flourishing and had many well-satisfied patients. However, there were still a few things nagging her. She was curious about the woman she had seen Dr. Right with. She was also concerned about his feelings for her. After all their time together, he never told her how he felt about her. She noticed that he stopped mentioning taking their relationship a step further and seemed perfectly satisfied with their relationship being hidden from all who knew them.

One day Jeff stopped by to see her. Over time he and Maggie had become friendlier, and he thought this would be a good time to approach her. Jeff wanted to tell Maggie about his feelings for her, but he was afraid of what her response would be. Jeff knew of Dr. Right and Maggie's relationship because a close friend had spoken with him about it. He desperately wanted to tell her about the man she was so into. Jeff had gotten word through the grapevine about Dr. Right's true intentions for Maggie. He admired her as an achiever who, in every sense of the word, was intelligent, ambitious, focused, and beautiful. Jeff knew Dr. Right was mistreating her and bragging about it. Dr. Right implicated that Maggie was too much in love with him, but he never wanted things to change; he would never leave his wife, and he never wanted Maggie or his wife to know what he was doing. Jeff felt it was time that someone told Maggie so everything could be put out into the open. Besides, this may open a few doors for him with her. Jeff was tall and handsome with straight, slightly curly hair and creamy, smooth, light chocolate skin. His physique was one that many a man envied. There were many young ladies who were attracted to him, but he wanted Maggie.

Jeff walked into Maggie's office, took a seat, and watched as Maggie scrolled through some patients' records on her computer. He hesitated but decided that if he didn't say anything now, he would not be able to later. He cleared his throat to get Maggie's attention, who had not even noticed that he was in the room. He mustered up the courage and began talking.

"Good morning Maggie," he said, waiting for a response. But Maggie only picked her head up, waved, and went back to looking at her files. So, Jeff decided to get straight to the point. "Excuse me, Maggie," with a little annoyance in his voice. "I have been watching you for a while, and I think there is something you need to know." Maggie never changed her focus. "I heard the rumors about you and Dr. Right," and he paused to wait for a response. She straightened up a little in her seat but did not want to give up her secret until she was sure of what he was talking about. "Dr. Right told a friend about your affair with him. He has been bragging about how you like to hang on to him, and that you believe anything he says." Jeff hesitated because of the realization that he had all of Maggie's attention, noticing the hurt in her eyes as he spoke ahead. Maggie did not say a word. Maggie did not want to believe him, but somehow, she knew he was telling the truth. Jeff decided to leave because, besides his intentions, he felt like a mean, cruel person. Maggie asked him to stay and continue. He told her about how Dr. Right had gotten his divorce and was staying with another woman while he had kept the relationship with Maggie. Dr. Right told his colleagues that his relationship with Maggie would never grow because she wasn't the kind of woman to be spent the rest of his life with. He wanted a woman who was not in competition with him and his area of expertise. She was speechless and wanted to let the tears fall, but Maggie held on to her image. Jeff saw the despair in her eyes and told her he was sorry but felt Maggie needed to know. Jeff wanted to hug her but dared not, instead, he simply told Maggie that if she ever needed anyone to talk to, she could call him. Jeff left his card and excused himself. Maggie nodded her head and said thank you.

Maggie was devastated but never allowed her torment to get in the way of her work. In fact, she worked harder. She tried to get in touch with the love of her life, but he had gone on a vacation without even telling her. When he returned, he called for his usual visit. Maggie waited to see if she could pick up on anything about his behavior or attitude. She realized this was his norm, and he saw nothing wrong with his actions. In his mind, he had rationalized this, and therefore, Dr. Right would never admit to any wrong doing on his part.

However, Maggie was allowing the anger to build up in her, and she could no longer sit back and not say anything. She waited until the right moment to ask this question that stayed on her mind since Jeff came into her office that very disturbing day. One night Dr. Right and Maggie sat beside each other, cuddling, kissing, and caressing until she got him to his weakest point. Maggie wanted him to be comfortable when she began her inquiry into the possibility of the other affair. She didn't want this to be drawn out, so she simply blurted out, "A friend of a friend of yours came by my office and told me some very uncomfortable news. At the time, I was very upset. But after time, I wondered if there was any truth to it?"

Dr. Right lay there with his eyes closed in a perfectly relaxed position. He was surprised that she was talking to him at this time but did not indicate where she was going with this. He asked, "If I may ask, what is disturbing you? What is it that you heard?"

She continued, "What are your intentions for us? How do you really feel about me? I need to know tonight." He didn't respond right away. The anger was starting to take over Maggie. She continued, rising and easing away from him just enough to make him pay attention. "Listen to me! I need to know because I have had a feeling that things will never change. I was told that you have a new woman and you are, in fact, divorced, which you seemed to neglect to tell me. Is this new woman who you want because you have been taking a lot of vacations lately? I think you need to tell me something! Are you just using me, or what? Tell me! Is this true? Why are you really here? Tell me!" Her voice had now elevated to the shouting point. She got up and started pacing the floor.

He sat up, grabbed his drink, and held his head down. He swallowed his drink. He began to talk to Maggie as if he genuinely regretted that she couldn't trust him. But his pride wouldn't allow him to go out like that. He was tired of playing the game with her. He admitted that he had no intentions of marrying her because she was too independent, self-reliant, and successful. He needed a woman who catered to his needs, be there for him, someone who was not competing with him. He admitted that he could never live with Maggie because of this and definitely not marry her. But he still loved her and did not want things to change between them. As Dr. Right's temper started to rise, his voice began to rise, and he stated that she could either take it or leave it.

This infuriated Maggie. She felt like someone had just hit her in her stomach. She wanted to run out of the room and cry alone, but she was too strong a woman for that. Besides, she wasn't finished. There were things she still needed to find out. She took a deep breath, closed her eyes and continued. She quietly asked, "Is there anything else I need to know?" She was giving him the opportunity to be a man to admit his mistakes.

Dr. Right looked at her and wondered if she knew anything else. He didn't want to tell her about the other woman. He leaned back on the couch and asked her, "What on earth could you possibly be talking about!" His smug attitude was followed by his sudden change of heart about being truthful. He began yelling about her imagining things, being jealous of nothing, and not spending enough time with him. Finally, to top it off, she must be doing something herself to suggest anything like that about him. He did everything to avoid admitting anything. At that point, Maggie picked up the glass from the table and threw it in his direction, barely missing his head. He ducked and moved out of the way. After the shock, Maggie started grabbing his things and moving toward the door. He started yelling, "Are you crazy!"

Maggie fired back, "What kind of game do you think this is? What kind of fool do you think I am? Even before I heard from my friend, I saw you sitting in the cafeteria with that woman laughing and talking. Is that the woman you are staying with now? Is she the one you have been taking on all your vacations lately? Answer me, and don't lie to me because I can't stand a liar! Just tell the truth! I have waited and waited for you. Now I hear that you only want me to always be the other woman. Are you crazy? Do you really expect me to be at your beck and call whenever you desire to do so? I don't need this! I can do better! Much better! I worshipped you and loved you. I dealt with you when you told me your marriage was failing. I waited for you to get your divorce. You proposed to me. You told me that we were getting married when the divorce was final. Now, you tell me that you did not intend to get married. Okay! I'm giving you one last chance. Tell me about the other woman."

He couldn't figure out who had given her this information. He was slightly confused. He had never seen Maggie act this way before. He came straight out and told her that there was another woman, but it was her fault that he considered being with her. After all, he was a man and couldn't let her intimidate him. In addition, as a man, he didn't owe her any explanation. She was just someone he had on the side, and she should've realized that a long time ago. He stood up for himself now with his back turned away from Maggie. As soon as the words finished coming out of his mouth, he heard a click and the cold touch of metal behind his head. Maggie pulled the trigger and shot into the wall. She told him that the next shot would be him. They stared at each other intensely. He was afraid and on the verge of tears, but, as a man, he couldn't let her see him go there. She was hurt and on the verge of tears, but she was making a point and couldn't show any fear. At that moment, Dr. Right felt he had nothing to lose, so he leaped toward her, and Maggie shot him in the leg. She dropped the gun and fell to the floor. He ran out as fast as he could. Dr. Right knew he was wrong for treating her in such a despicable manner, so he never pressed charges. Besides, he never wanted the stories of his relationship to come out. Maggie did have to face the authorities and go before the judge. The judge gave her a pass because of her position in the community but required her to volunteer at a battered women's facility.

After all of the confusion and drama Maggie had gone through with Dr. Right, she began to humble herself. In addition, in her working with the victims, her attitude changed along with her empathy for others. One day while working with a young lady, Virginia walked in to talk to the same woman Maggie was working with. They saw each other and hesitated to greet. The information Virginia needed was important, so she took a seat and quietly waited. When the session ended, Maggie made her way across the room to Virginia. Maggie acknowledged her, spoke softly to her, and told her how glad she was to see her. They both felt awkward. Maggie had been reflecting on how badly she had treated Virginia in their childhood and for not being more understanding of her troubles. After her encounters with Dr. Right, Virginia had been on her mind. She had vowed that when the opportunity presented itself, she would apologize—the time had finally presented itself, and Maggie didn't know how to deal with it. The two of them stood there silently until Virginia spoke up. She apologized for interrupting and was about to leave. Maggie took that time to ask Virginia if she could sit awhile. They sat across from one another; both did not know what to do next. Maggie suddenly jumped up out of her seat and hugged Virginia. Virginia embraced her friend back. Now they both were in tears but continued to hold on to each other even tighter. When they composed themselves, they sat down, never letting go of each other's hands. They both had gotten the news about the other and now felt they could be there for each other. This is a real friendship. Since their work day was over, they went to a diner where they sat and talked until late into the night. From that day forth, they gained mutual respect and became even closer friends as adults.

Comments:

There is a serious problem in our communities. It is a lack of empathy and understanding of others. It is especially apparent when it comes to females in abusive relationships. Think about it! What would you do if you saw your friend, sister, aunt, or mother heading for, involved in, or trying to get out of a bad relationship? I have seen so many situations when people will simply snub others who happen to be trapped in an unhealthy partnership. If they have not experienced anything like this or think you haven't, you don't understand the effects it can have on a person. The first words that come out of your mouth are, "Oh no! That will never happen to me." Then comes the, "I would do this, or she should do this, or I wouldn't take that." They have no words of real resolution or help. But anticipate or predict what will happen to you because you're stupid. These struggles are not authentic to a person until you are the person experiencing them. Facing the truth is one thing and getting away or making your mind up to get away is another. It is no easy task in most cases. These problems have no solution, like a math problem of two times two is four. Now it is a matter of following your heart or your brain. Each person is different, each couple is different and our backgrounds. God didn't run us through an assembly line like a factory. In reality, we are all different, have free will, and make distinguished decisions. A person may recognize abuse the first time and get away before it escalates. On the hand, for some, it may take years. As a community, we need a better listening and sympathy ear for whenever the victims are ready to make that move.

There are several ways abuse presents itself and can affect a person differently. Every person in this world who is involved in any relationship will see some form in their lifetime. It could be verbal abuse, physical abuse, financial abuse, cheating, abandonment, rape, or someone who disrespects you on any level. Most people get involved with a person with blinders on not knowing everything they need to know about each. The four lessons here are: (1.) Never say never because absolute words can come back to haunt you. (2.) Never get involved with a married man because, in most cases, you will come out on the short end. (3.) Never get involved in a relationship that is not equally yoked or where the other person feels superior to you. You may be so mesmerized that your partner can easily take advantage of you. (4.)

Remember that when you learn a lesson, help others to grow from your experience. As stated in Philippians 2:3, there is value in helping others. Helping others will be a reminder to you and other victims or potential victims because God has given you a testimony to pass on to others.

When Does It Stop?

She cried out for help, but no one listened.
She went to her mother, but there was little she
could do.
She went to her sisters, but they said it was
none of their business.
She went to her minister. He prayed and said
everything would be okay.
But in the middle of a storm, she wondered
When does it stop?

As the days passed, the situation got worst.
The stalking and the appearances from out of
the blue.
The intimidation and the uncertainty of how
he would feel.
The strikes to her body with his hand or even a
shoe.
But in the middle of the trauma, all she could
think of was, When does it stop?

With no hope, she turned to God.
Before the unforeseen argument, she turned to
God.

In the middle of the confusion, she prayed to
God.
After it was over, she thanked God.
But still wondered when does it stop.

As the days passed, there was less tension in
the air.
God listened and gave her the armor to push
away the confusion and fear.
In the end, God bought closure her way.
Finally, God touched his heart, and the man
just walked away.

"But you, God, see the trouble of the afflicted; you consider their grief and take it in hand. The victims commit themselves to you; you are the helper of the fatherless."

—*Psalms 10:14*

Extremities

Dear God,

Through this journal, I am expressing one of the most difficult experiences of my life. I thank you, God, for being there and hearing my prayers. You guided my steps; gave me the opportunities and the common sense to finally get out of a very life-threatening relationship.

March 1st

Dear Journal,

Loretta and I went to a Jazz Club for a girl's night out last night. The club was live and crowded. The music was amazing. We watched the first session and were about to leave when a guy asked if he could sit at our table. His name was Willie. As a gesture of thanks, he bought us some drinks. Loretta excused herself from the table to go and buy one of the CDs that the band was selling. The conversation started between us. I don't know who said what, but it was very engaging. The chemistry between us was magical and enticing. Before the night was over, we had exchanged numbers, and I was flying high. I thought I had met a man that I may actually be a true prospect. I went home and looked over my prospect check List; at that point, he fulfilled seven out of ten of my desires. He had a great job, handsome, charming, polite, respectful, educated, and he loved jazz. I'll get back to you later. Oh my God! This is him calling me.

March 7th

Dear Journal,

I'm so sorry that I have been neglecting you, but I have been having the time of my life. Willie took me to dinner three times this week. After I got home, he would call me, and we would talk well into the night. I enjoyed every moment. It was like living in a dream. The only problem I was having was that he was a bit controlling. When we ordered our food, he did it for me, saying that he had a good choice. When I spoke up, he would simply lean over, kiss my hand or cheek, and say, "Trust me. You'll love it." I decided to let the man be a man. On the third dinner date, I took it upon myself to order for both of us while he went to Men's Room. My personality would not rest without standing up for myself in this subtle way. I didn't think it would bother him, but he sternly told me never to do that again. He strongly announced that this was a man's duty and I needed to let him be the man. I didn't quite understand what was happening, but I know that sometimes I can take things for granted. I'm used to people being on an equal basis, and it shouldn't matter that he is a man. I was a little upset, but a thought passed through my mind that may be I am being too picky. In the past, I left other guys for less than this and ended up alone. I decided to let it go and relax.

March 10th

Dear Journal,

Even though I tried to conceal my feelings from that dinner date, I couldn't. I guess he saw that my mood had changed. The next day I received a huge boutique of roses and a card. On the card, there was a beautiful gold necklace. I was so excited. I called him and expressed my gratitude so much that he felt I was alright with his behavior. I wasn't, but the gifts took away some of the anger. That night we went to a stepper's set. A lot of his friends were there, and I loved to dance. I never knew there were rules for steppers, too. The first rule was to follow his lead and try not to embarrass him. If you have ever been to a Stepper's Club in Chicago, the real Steppers don't have time for those who will make them look bad on the dance floor. If you mess up one time, you will be sitting down the rest of the night. Willie and I danced a couple of times, and then he disappeared. Willie found us a table and left when he saw a few of his friends talking across the room. I was sitting there, watching everyone else on the floor. I waited while he laughed and talked with everyone in his click that he knew for what seemed like forever. Finally, a guy came up and asked me to dance. I did dance with the guy for two or three songs. One of the songs was a slow song which meant that we were dancing close. I looked over at our table, and there was Willie. He was sitting there with a cool, blank look on his face. I didn't know what to make of it, so I told the guy I had to leave and walked off the dance floor. When I got to the table, Willie got up and said he was ready to go. He barely said a word in the car on the way home. He apologized for his actions when we pulled in front of my house and explained that when we were out together, I was never dancing with another man without asking him first. In his eyes, that was disrespectful to him. He was embarrassed by my doing that, especially in front of his friends. I wasn't used to all of these rules, but I went along with it because it wasn't a big deal. We probably won't be going out dancing anymore because I wasn't going to be sitting around at the table by myself while he ran around with his friends.

April 1st

Dear Journal,

Willie and I were together more and more. We had our problems, but I tried to look pass all the rules he had for me. Although, I will say that most of the rules were bought up after we were with his friends or after they left. This night, he invited some friends over to watch a basketball game. My friends didn't like Willie and wouldn't come over if he was there. I went into the kitchen to get away from them. His friend James came in there about five minutes later. We talked for a minute until I saw that he was stepping out of bounds by asking me to meet him at a hotel. I left him in there and never said a word to Willie because I didn't want to hear any more rules. I later went to a friend and asked if I should tell Willie about the conversation. We agreed that it would be best if I didn't.

April 7th

Dear Journal,

One day, James was mocking Willie and told him about the conversation. James told Willie that we were to meet up the evening they talked. Willie stormed out and called me. However, that night I had gone out with my friends for a birthday drink. By now, James was gone, and Willie couldn't get in touch with me.

In his mind, what James said must be the truth. Later that night, I looked at my phone and saw it had died. When it charged up, I saw all the missed calls. I took a deep breath and put the phone on my chest before calling back. I asked God to give me strength! He asked where I had been. I told him. He wanted to know if he could come by. I had no idea what was about to happen.

He came by, and we had a little chit-chat. As we talked more and more, I noticed that he seemed to be digging for something. I decided to let him talk. Finally, he got around to it. James' name came up, and he asked me directly if I had ever gone out with him. I said, "No!" I was upset because of the insulting way he went about it. He didn't believe me. He told me I was lying and that he knew that I met James at a hotel. After that and my denial, he went into interrogation mode. He acted like I was under arrest and continued questioning me throughout the night. Around two in the morning, this method wasn't working for him.

He grabbed my arm and told me that I better stop lying. He commented that I should tell him the truth because he just needed to know. He left that night and said he would call me later.

April 10th

Dear Journal,

I was so angry that I decided I needed to get out of this whole relationship. It took a couple of days for me to accept any calls from him, but that didn't stop him from calling. There were calls back-to-back all day long. It was driving me crazy! I still would not answer the phone. Then I walked out of my house one morning, and there he was, standing by my car with flowers in hand and a big smile. He said you can't get rid of me that easy. I love you too much! I know you are still mad, but I'm sorry! He then tried to kiss my lips, but I turned my head. He continued saying, "Come here and let me talk to you. I talked to James, and he said he met you there, but nothing happened." I told him that was a lie. So, he tried again to get me to admit I met him. Then suddenly, his smile and charm disappeared. He started walking away, then turned around and slapped me so hard that I fell to the ground. He said, "Now, I know you met him, and you better start telling me the truth. Get your ass off the ground before somebody comes by." I was in shock. I had never been slapped in my entire life, and I started crying. He grabbed my face and said, "Do you really want these people to see you get your ass beat. Now stop all that noise, and wipe your face. And get your ass out of here and go to work. I'll be by later to pick you up and answer the phone! I don't want to have to go looking for you either!" With that, he walked back to his car and drove off. I pulled myself up and left the flowers on the ground.

All that day, I couldn't figure it out. I was unable to concentrate on my work. I felt a little secure when he left that morning, but I knew he would be back after work. I pondered over calling the police. I didn't think that anyone would pay any attention to me. Willie was well-known in the community. He had a lot of connections with the police, leaders, and many politicians in the area. I didn't want to involve my family or friends because I was ashamed. I didn't want them to know about the position I was in. I thought about leaving town and running away, but I didn't want to look like a coward or leave without some kind of provisions. So, I sat unsure of how to handle this crazy and threatening situation I found myself in.

That night, Willie called my house. We talked, but he could tell that I wasn't the same. He apologized over and over. He finally admitted that he could be out of control sometimes, but he vowed that it would never happen again. I told him I needed time for myself. I needed to think about all that had happened between us. He agreed and asked if he could just call me to check on me. I saw nothing wrong with that, so I agreed.

April 14th

Dear Journal,

Life is much more peaceful, but I still have some decisions. This man continues to call me. Also, I'm not sure, but I find it a coincidence that whenever I go out, I see him. I wondered if he was stalking me. I went to the grocery store on Saturday afternoon. He was there. He didn't even live in the area. In fact, he lived all the way across town. Why would he be shopping over here? This whole ordeal has taken part of my faith and strength. I was more and more fearful. I always looked over my shoulders and was always on edge. It was very unsettling, and I found that I could not even sit still. I ate nervously, and I always had to be doing something. He still called me and continuously asked if I would go out with him. I kept saying I needed more time. This was my way to avoid facing the inevitable because I knew I shouldn't have any more to do with him. I knew I had to follow my first mind about two things. First, if a man hits you once it will happen again. Second, I really felt that he was stalking me. In addition, why is he still calling me? He seemed to be forcing his will on me, and to give up would mean he lost his control. It made me think that he would never give up and that I was prey forever. I knew I needed to call the police, but I was afraid that it wouldn't do any good. I needed an order of protection. However, he hadn't approached me in a while.

April 29th

Dear Journal,

After many calls, charming words and promises, I gave in and said I would go out with him one more time. It was my birthday. I thought things might have changed because we had been apart for a while. Plus, I needed to relax, have some companionship and enjoy myself for once in a long time. When Willie came, he was driving a new luxury car. I'll admit I was impressed. He was attentive and accommodating. He literally made me feel like a queen. We laughed and talked. It felt like none of the things I had been fearful of ever existed. He told me that he had a gift for me. He presented the title and the keys to the car to me. The car was my present. I was afraid to take, but I was also afraid not to. I didn't want the mood to turn into an argument. We spent the night together. Again, I was not sure that this was the right thing to do, but I didn't want to cause an argument.

The next morning, all hell broke loose. The gift, the dinner, and all his charm were just another plot to get me to finally admit the truth that I had an affair with James. We got up the next morning, and we went out to breakfast. We both had to go to work, so I felt at ease because I thought that this date was almost over. I felt that I could relax because he would be gone soon. As was the norm for him, he eased into the conversation by talking about his friends, and then James' name came up. My antennas went up because it meant trouble every time this name came up. I didn't say anything. He went on talking, trying to get me to say something. I decided that we should leave. He agreed. However, when we got to the car, he insisted on driving. He started again with the interrogation. He wanted to know if I slept with James. He said I hadn't been with him for a while, so I must have been sleeping with someone. I denied everything and asked him to take me to work. Praying all the time and counting the blocks to my job, I thought about if I ever got out of this car, Willie would never see me again. Life is too short to go through all of this drama. Then, before I knew it, he grabbed my hair and slammed my head against the dashboard. He pulled the car over and started choking me. He told me that I was going to stop lying to him and I was going to tell him the truth today. He started driving again. I saw the police driving behind us and thought that would be my way out. I glanced down at the locks while he continued to rant and rave about how I made him do that to me. The doors were unlocked.

When we slowed at the lights, I jumped out while the car was still moving. This got the attention of the police, and they turned the lights and siren on Willie. One policeman spoke with me, and the other talked to Willie.

I was crying uncontrollably and shaking. I told the policeman that I was in fear for my life. I explained that Willie was holding me against my will, had choked me, and threatened to kill me. Willie, on the other hand, was calm and composed. He told the policeman that I was overreacting. He said he had bought me this car and we had just finished celebrating my birthday. He gave the policeman the impression that we had a minor disagreement. All the while looking over at me, saying, "Baby, you alright?" He turned to the policeman he was talking to and said, "She'll be alright! I'll just take her home so she can rest." But the charm didn't work this time. The policemen talked with each other and made the decision. They told him to give me the keys and told me to go on.

I took that as a sign and went straight to the police station to file a report. When it came time for me to go to court, I was there, and so was he. He still denied everything, but the judge put a restraining order on him. The fact that he couldn't come within 300 feet relieved some of my tension. I went home and tried to sleep. I still wasn't comfortable. I called a friend of mine to come stay with me for a few days. However, I knew she couldn't stay forever, and after a few days, she had to go. This is a problem I had to deal with alone. Willie had been calling but not from his phone. There were messages left from how sorry he was to how he will never do it again to how he just got mad to how he wanted to make it up to me. He went from that to the other extreme of - he better not catch me or he was going to kill me to how he didn't really hurt me. He finally went to the point where he felt that I got him in trouble for nothing. He called me a drama queen and said he wanted his car back. I called the police, but they responded that there was nothing they could do as long as he doesn't come into the parameters that he was restricted from. They suggested I change my number. I did, but he got that number too.

July 8th

Dear Journal,

Today I went to talk to my friend Mildred. She heard about the problems I was experiencing. She had worked with many other women in similar situations. Willie was still calling, and it was driving me crazy. After we talked, she gave me the simplest advice-record, block, and report. Record the calls if I should happen to pick up the phone. Block if you recognize his number or any numbers he might have used in the past. Report and write down the number of calls along with recordings. She ordered me to have all this written down if and when I must go to court. The most important thing she said was to avoid calls as much as I could because it was his way of controlling me. Eventually, the calls stopped.

July 26th

Dear Journal,

Willie stopped calling, but he found other ways to get me. Sometimes I would see him outside of my job. (He always stays the required distance away). He still would send unsigned flowers, gifts, cards, and letters with the note saying I love you! You know who. He got frustrated after he saw that I wouldn't give him the time of day. One day, when I was unlocking the door to go in the house with an armful of groceries, Willie came from behind and pushed me in. I fell and slid across the floor. The groceries fell everywhere. I looked up into his eyes, and he looked so frightening. I tried scrambling, but he was right over me with a gun. I couldn't understand what he was saying because the gun had all of my attention. He was yelling and screaming something about me being a slut and a liar. He spit on me and then demanded that I get up and go with him.

We went out to his car, and he told me to drive. He spoke very little but gave directions with a gun still pointed at me. We finally got to James' house. Willie forced me out of the car and pushed me to the door. He appeared to be going through some kind of psychotic breakdown. James and I sat there while he walked back and forth, telling us that today the truth would be told, or somebody won't have to worry about tomorrow. James started trying to tell him that nothing had happened and that it was all a lie. Willie didn't believe him. Then he turned to me, and I denied it again. He pointed the gun at my head and pulled the trigger, but nothing happened. James grabbed him from behind and knocked him to the floor. I took off running while they fought. I opened the door, saw a neighbor's kid peeking out, and begged him to let me in. I called 911, and they finally came in what seemed like hours. Willie broke away from James and started searching for me. He had no idea that I was still in the area, so he ran out of the building and down the street. I saw him from the window. I also saw the police coming down the street. With my description of him, the police picked him up and came to the neighbor's house to get me. I pressed charges, and they locked him up pending trial for violation of the court order. Attempted murder and kidnapping were added to the other charge. The judge threw the book at him. It turned out that this was not the first time Willie had been before this judge. He received so much time that he would not be eligible for parole for 10 years. I left that courtroom so elated with a big smile on my face. I felt like I had won the lottery, only it was the freedom of my spirit. I literally felt as light as a feather.

Comments:

Extreme behaviors of this type of abuser thrive on keeping his victim, his significant other, off balance and unsure of the love he claims to have for her. The control method of confusion develops through the abuser presenting themselves as charming, caring, available, helpful, and responsible on the one hand. On the other hand, he can be demanding, unyielding, chauvinist, and a regulator of her every move. Beware of these abusers because they can seriously damage your self-confidence. This is their goal because, in the end, they want complete control of all decision-making. The extreme cases will put you in the position of being isolated from family members and friends, unable to make decisions on all levels, and the woman having to ask about every move she makes. This abuser is exceedingly dangerous because they are unpredictable. The victim never knows what to expect from them and usually is constantly on edge. The victim tends to walk on eggshells when they are together because one wrong word can trigger a switch in his behavior. Think of this abuser as Dr. Jekyll and Mr. Hyde. As Dr. Jekyll, he can be loving, kissing, accommodating, and respectful. As Mr. Hyde, he can be life-threatening and have a bully mentality.

Several points need to be made about the extreme behavior abuser that you should take heed to. First, a relationship should be a shared experience. A couple should make decisions together in a respectful manner. When one person makes all decisions, it is belittling and disrespectful to their partner's intelligence. In this story, Willie wanted complete control and never listened unless it agreed with him. This showed that he considered her less than him and made rules for her, but there weren't for him. Second, if a man does not trust you, forget about the love because this is a warning sign of troubles ahead. You cannot make a person trust you! In addition, mistrust can be like a rolling snowball you have no control over. It can grow and grow over time. It may not ever be resolved, but it continues to get worst. Finally, physical abuse and even death can result from these extreme behaviors. The abuser is uncontrollable and feels he has a right to do what he does. They don't many times have a filter on how far they can go.

The Myth

The myth is that the abused woman can just
walk away.
The myth is that the abused woman likes it or
she's weak.
The myth is that the abused woman asked for
it that day.
The myth is that it was the abused woman's
fault or she was out of her league.
In all facets of this scenario, the victim is
blamed in every way.

Outsiders! Examine your hearts and minds.
Things are not as easy as they seem.
Abusers are people who thrive in causing
havoc that crosses the normal lines.
Abusers need to control and have power over
their team.
Where are the consequences and the blame for
his crimes?

The fight is about the abuser keeping control
and being powerful.
The fight is about the victim submitting to her
god and being grateful.

The arena for this action is small, one-minded,
and allows for little or no growth.
However, the abuser does not realize that his
decisions are not best for both.
The abuser does not allow for the fullest
potential of the relationship to flow.

These relationships are not equally yoked,
where one of them always settles for less.
Don't judge the abused one because often it's
hard to get out of their mess.
Many times, they cannot just walk away.
An abused woman fears what may happen day
to day
Talk to a woman in that position and see that
she's not weak.

In all facets of this scenario, the trapped victim
is blamed every step of the way.
When the victims finally sees the light and gets
away.
Learn from it and thank God- that's progress.
Do positive things, think positive, and God
does the rest.
God has a plan throughout all of your traumas
and regrets

His time is not the same as your time.
Listen and talk to God. It will clear your mind.
Because the myths are man-made and will
destroy you down the line.

"As for a person who stirs up division, after warning him once and then twice; have nothing more to do with him, knowing that such a person is warped and sinful; he is self-condemned."

—Titus 3:10-11

The Myths of Domestic Abuse

Imagine sitting in a room with a group of teenagers who feel like they know all the answers. Wow! These girls look like they are going to be a handful. There are about ten young ladies in this group who are at risk or have been in situations that made them vulnerable to the streets. It was part of my community service to help these young ladies. The judge said I needed to see the reality and the possible devastation of my decisions. He said to me, "Ms. Faye Henderson, you look like a woman with a good head on your shoulders. I'm giving you one last chance. But if I ever see you in my courtroom again, I'm locking you up." Then he gave me two years of probation and one hundred hours of community service. I had been in a bad place and made some bad decisions which almost got a man killed. My decision was justifiable, but this wasn't my first time in the domestic court, and I kept running into the same judge. He had a soft spot in his heart for my circumstances, but his patience was at the breaking point. He sent me to the center to work with this group of girls as a mentor for domestic violence awareness.

I arrived at the center early and sat quietly in the back of the room to observe them as they came in. They came in one by one with attitudes so bad that it looked like they could chew nails. One girl rolled her eyes at me. She walked over to another and said, "Who is that? I hope we don't have another person coming in here trying to tell us more boring stuff." These two girls, Charlene and Audrey, seemed to be friends; they sat next to each other and started getting on their phones, texting. Suddenly, Charlene started yelling, "I know that b---- didn't say that about me. Gabrielle put this out about me f----king her boyfriend, and she wanted to fight. I can't help it that I do him better than she can and in ways she won't." Charlene then posted her willingness to fight Gabrielle whenever she wanted to. Then she laughed and turned around to show the message to Audrey. Audrey read it and gave her a word of warning, telling her, "Girl, why you are sweating over that no-good negro. Pretty soon, he will be jumping on you like he is doing her. You know he threw her down the stairs last week. She'll be in here later, and you need to let that go!" Charlene responded, "Oh no! I'm not worried about her or him. He does that stuff to her, not me. But he did tell me that I better not touch her. I told him, if she touched me, I'm GOING to touch her in a way that she will never forget!" Now she had drawn a crowd because everybody in the class could hear her and began to get closer.

Audrey glanced down at her phone and started smiling. She stood up and announced, "Well, while you are talking about fighting, I'll be getting my hair and nails done. I told my man that he must take care of me if he wants to keep me. See, I don't play. He told me that he'll picking me up after this!" Another girl yelled from the other side of the room, "He should! You just told me that you paid his cell phone bill and he never paid you back." Audrey fired back, "You need to mind your own business!" All the other girls laughed at her because they all knew the story. Audrey always paid his bills and he always came back with a lie, one after the other, about why he couldn't pay back.

Gabrielle was the last to enter the room. She wore dark glasses and walked with a limp, struggling with each step. There was a sudden silence as she walked to her seat. Charlene started to get out of her seat and headed in her direction. I anticipated the situation and was about to offer some interference, but Charlene retreated as the counselor entered the room. Ms. Cooper stopped and gave Charlene a stern look. Ms. Cooper was always ahead of the trouble. The girls knew that and were aware of the consequences if they crossed the line with her. Ms. Cooper walked to the front of the room and announced, "There will no problems today. Right! If you have an issue with anything or anybody today you may step out of the room and sit in my office until I arrive. Again! There will be no problems in here today! Is that clear?" Ms. Cooper did not play around, and they all knew it. She stood there quietly waiting for a response or for anyone to leave. No one moved or said a word. I was surprise that her very presence commanded respect and the girls gave it to her.

I stood up so she could notice me and was about to introduce myself. She simply put up a finger, letting me know she had acknowledged me, so I sat back down. I felt like one of the girls even though I was about the same age as Ms. Cooper. Ms. Cooper stood there for a minute to give the girls enough time, and then she began to speak. "Good morning! I want everyone to remember why you are here. Now I need a minute to speak to our guest. In the meantime, I need you to get yourselves together. That means putting up all cell phones and getting your minds together. Oh! By the way, I heard everything that was being said before entering. I don't want that behavior again. Do we understand each other?" There was no response. There was only silence. With that, she walked over to me and introduced herself. I told her why I was there. She explained that she had reluctantly agreed to have me work with them but pointed out that this would be temporary and with conditions. She wanted to see how the girls would react to me. Ms. Cooper asked about the approach I would be using with the girls and if I had ever dealt with girls like hers before. I was puzzled by this unexpected investigation; I thought I would just present myself and give some helpful advice. That would have been enough for me. When the judge ordered me to do this, I didn't know what I was getting into. I respectfully informed Ms. Cooper that I would like to introduce myself, explain why I was there, and answer some questions. She stopped me and said, "Look, I will give you more time to think about a plan. You see these girls! They are very smart and will read right through you. You won't get anywhere with them. From what I hear, you are to complete one hundred hours of community service, and the things you have just said won't get you through one hour. This won't be easy. I've talked to my supervisor, for today, I will work with them while you jot down some ideas. After they leave, I will look them over. I will help you organize them. I think this will help not only them but you too." I didn't say a word. I took out some paper and started writing.

Ms. Cooper and I devised a plan to get the young ladies' attention after her session. "No long story to showboat because they will tune you out. No fantasy stories because they know more about life than you think. Finally, don't sugarcoat the truth because they will see right through it." She further advised me to discuss my truth and struggles to reel them in. From there, she suggested working together to help the girls better understand abuse and its reality. These young ladies were chosen for this program because they were either victims of abuse; they accepted it as a way of life or abused others because that was all they knew. Ms. Cooper was unsure of me, but she was hopeful. She pointed out that at this time in the girls' life, they don't fully see or understand the consequences of their circumstances. She really cared about her group and wanted them to gain the knowledge to live a more productive and safe lives. She felt this help could enable them to live long, happy lives without any hurdles.

That night, I researched until I came across some myths about abuse. This would be my focus of learning. I knew I had to find a way to get them to trust me. I came up with Plan A and

Plan B. Plan A - I will tell them why I was there and my journey with abusive relationships and the law. I knew I would have to be real, but I wasn't sure if my reality would positively affect me. After all, I did try to kill a man or two and almost went to jail. Plan B - Present scenarios about the myths of abuse and discuss their feelings.

The next morning, I got dressed and picked up the makeup kit on my dresser. That's when it clicked. I arrived at my destination early and went into the ladies' room to prepare myself. I put on just enough makeup to get their attention. I had spoken to Ms. Cooper, but I didn't tell her the extent that I was going. She had already started talking to the girls when I walked into the room. I made my face look as if I had a black eye, but no one could see it with my sunglasses on. I walked in quietly and took a seat. As soon as Ms. Cooper finished the announcements to them, she introduced me. I now had the floor. I wrote my first myth on the board.

Day 1 - Myth 1: "If domestic abuse is a rare occurrence, it's not dangerous."

(All abuse is dangerous. Subtle aggression such as gaslighting, critical judgment, put-downs, and restrictions are all the stepping-stones to becoming more abusive in the future. A rare occurrence of abuse is still a way of controlling the victim and sets up the overall abusive dynamic in the relationship.)

As I looked around the room, everyone paid about as much attention to me as the man on the moon. I announced to them, "My name is Fay Henderson. I am going to be perfectly honest with you. I am the victim of a lifetime of abuse. My situation resulted in me getting arrested and going before the judge for attempted murder. Not once, but twice. The charges were reduced because of the level of pain the judge gathered that I had experienced. This is my last chance to make things right. My job here will be to help you become aware of the myths about abuse and the signs to be beware in relationships. This will help as a preventive measure. Hopefully, when we complete our session, I want you to understand how easy it is to get into these situations and how hard it is to get out of them. This downward spiral many victims have experienced can change a person's life completely, even to the point of death for you or your partner. Our first steps will be to understand the myths said about domestic abuse." Out of the corner of my eye, I saw a girl lean over to whisper something to her friend, lean back, and then roll her eyes. I continued talking and asked, "How many of you know someone in a bad relationship or have been victims of abuse yourselves?" No one responded. Then there was a remark behind my back, "Does she really think we are going to tell her our business?" At that point, my anger was starting to build up because, over the years, I developed a short fuse, and I don't like being ignored. I turned around to face the young woman who was talking to her friend and texting another. I snatched off my glasses. My voice became loud. I looked directly at her and said, "Am I bothering you? As I said, I am here because I must be here. But don't get it twisted. I feel this is very important for you and for me. Now if you don't want to listen, then be quiet for others to hear." She saw my blackeye and was stunned by the way I had come back at her. The bored look on everyone's face changed to a more serious glare. Charlene spoke up for the group, "Don't nobody have to take this from you!" Ms. Cooper quickly intervened. The glare she gave us made the girl put their phones up immediately and to be respectful. She pointed out we equally wrong. The look she gave me reminded me that I needed to handle this better or that I could leave. After she checked all of us, she asked me to carry on. I pretended as if I was embarrassed about my eye and apologized for my behavior. I point to my eye and said this is a not real but it is part of my story. I can still feel the pain to this day and every time I talk about it, it hurts. I began to share my story.

"It was in the summer of 2015 I decided to leave my boyfriend of 10 years because I had reached my limit. I had been stalked, beaten, belittled, and tortured for at least nine of those years. Even though I knew better, I told him. Big mistake! You cannot tell the person who has controlled every aspect of your life that you are leaving. That's when I got one of the worst moments of my life. He cried. He apologized. He switched to yelling and belittling me. He said, 'You know I need you. You can't go nowhere. I run this. What am I supposed to do?" I grabbed my bag to leave, he grabbed me by the arm and threw me back on the floor. He accused me of cheating on him. He said he knew that I was going to my new man. He got in my face, and he wanted me to admit it. I had gotten tired of all the drama and started yelling back at him, but I knew he had me right where he wanted me. I had been through this before. Now I was defying him, so he grabbed me by my neck, and even though I struggled, he dragged me to the bathroom and pushed my head into the toilet. I felt I had no choice. I agreed not to go and apologized. He was still upset but eventually calmed down. He made me get in bed with him. He went to sleep with his arm around me to ensure I didn't leave. When I thought he was sound asleep, I started inching my way out of the bed. He moaned and asked where I was going. I told him I was going to the bathroom. He told me to hurry up. I went to the bathroom and looked around. I saw a full liquor bottle on the table next to the bathroom. I took it into the room and quickly burst it upside his head. I grabbed my things and ran out of the house. He tried to chase me, but his injuries made him fall to the floor. Someone reported the commotion to the police, and they had to take him to the hospital. They later picked me up because he said I tried to kill him. That day was one of the most hurtful days of my life."

I had gotten so lost in my story that I felt alone in the room. I paused and glanced around the room, realizing I had an audience. I had everyone's undivided attention. I decided this would be the perfect time to ask my questions. I reiterated, "This is my story. How often do you think this kind of thing happen? Some remarks implicated that the women asked for it and one person even said I shouldn't have made him mad. In other words, do you think this is rare? Do you think this type of life is dangerous?" The hands went up. Some didn't believe me. Some empathized with me and understood. Others clarified that that wouldn't be them; he would be dead or they just wouldn't put up with that behavior. I explained to them this was a real story whether they believed it or not. Now I moved on to the second stage of this session by talking about these incidents in hope of preventing them from going through what I did. I felt a good feeling streaming through my body and continued. I gave them the statistics from the National Coalition Against Domestic Violence (NCADV – [1978]). I decided to highlight two points a day to further emphasize my message.

- 1 in 3 women and 1 in 4 men is a victim of some form of physical violence by an intimate partner during their lifetime.

I had them stand in groups of three and stressed that one of the three at least could be victims. This exercise included Ms. Cooper and myself.

- Domestic violence is most common among women aged 18-24 and 25-34.

I called attention to this fact because age in domestic violence has no limit. It could happen to young ladies as young as fourteen or as old as sixty. There is no magic age of when it could start or stop. However, it usually happens with the young who are just starting to get into relationships. They are often unaware of the signs of abuse and can be blinded by men they think they are in love with.

At the end of my first day, only half of my audience paid attention. All my talk meant nothing but something they had to do to stay on Ms. Cooper's good grace. We talked later, and

Ms. Cooper advised me not to lose faith and exercise more patience. She knew girls needed these lessons, and she told me she would have another talk with them the next day. She informed me that many of them are there because they have already experienced some form of physical violence. She told me that they weren't ignoring me, but they were either in denial; they didn't want to face their situations, or they were struggling with the decision of how and when to get out.

Day 2 - Myth 2: Victims have certain types of personality traits or are a class of people that seek out abuse.

There is no one type of person who is a victim of abuse. Victims can come from any background, class, wealthy or poor. They do not have a personality disorder or mental illness to be susceptible to an abusive relationship. Abusers are the ones who are responsible for the abusive relationship.

When I got home, I removed my glasses and washed the makeup off my face. I decided to use another approach. I returned and bought a stack of notebooks so the girls could write. The next day I gave everyone a notebook and a pen. I began my session by underlining the words on the board I had written out earlier. Next, I asked questions, "Have you ever been a victim or seen a person being violated? How did you feel? What did you do? I don't want you to say anything right now. I want you to write it out." I knew someone would say they never experienced it. I directed them to pretend they had to create a scenario for me. But to my surprise, they immediately started writing. While I had them listen to a song by Tracy Chapman - Behind the Wall. The singer in this song hears the screaming of a woman behind the wall as her husband beats her. She tells how the police refuse to interfere as the woman cries helplessly. In the last verse, the ambulance arrives to take the woman away as the police tell everyone to go back to sleep. When they finished writing, I gave them a copy of these lyrics to reflect on:

Last night, I heard the screaming

Then a silence that chilled my soul

I prayed that I was dreaming,

When I saw the ambulance in the road

And the police said,

'I'm here to keep the peace.'

Will the crowd disperse?

I think we all could use some sleep.

I began the discussion with a question, "What kind of person goes through this type of drama?" Before anyone could respond, I added a few things to think about. "Would this person most likely be poor or rich; young or old; educated or a high school dropout; or a loud or quiet person?" I continued, "Do you think abusers and victims of abuse learn to accept abuse as a way of life because they grew up around this type of violent behavior?" I wanted to paint a picture in their minds of the typical victim. I gave the assignment to draw a picture describing the victim and the abuser. They had to choose from the adjectives written on the board to tell what kind of person they most likely were. I walked around the room and observed what they were writing down. They all wrote what I thought they would. It was apparent that they could only see things that were around their age. Even those who wrote about other age groups, they did not think it could happen to people who are financially blessed. After some time, I called the group back together. I asked if anyone would like to share. I told them we are here to learn to listen and heal. There was always one in the group who loved to talk; it was Michelle. Michelle let us all know that it was her life and would never let anyone do anything to her.

At that moment, Gabrielle walked in late again. With her bloodshot eyes as she walked with a little limp. She found her seat and looked away from everyone. Michelle focused now on Gabrielle and pointed an accusing finger at her, and said, "That's a victim! I saw her being screamed at by him, and she did nothing but take it. I figured that she wanted it. Standing there looking stupid! Then he started choking her, and she didn't even make a sound. How stupid can you be? I would just walk away." Gabrielle sat there with her eye fixed on the wall. It was justified if she wanted to leave but stayed. This was a safe haven for her. I've seen this with other victims. The school was the one place where she knew he couldn't bother her. It was safe until it was time to go. There is a certain relief for the time being there in that moment you arrive, but the anxiety kicks in when the time comes to go home. She couldn't afford to be put out of class for fear, and then where would she go? Ms. Cooper walked into the class as Michelle continued commenting on

Gabrielle. Michelle stopped. Ms. Cooper took over the class and told everyone to write what had happened. Then she told them that we would talk more about it tomorrow, and no one was to say a word for the rest of the time.

All of us reasoned that Gabrielle was caught up in a dangerous position. However, our hands were tied because she would never acknowledge anything about the trauma. Gabrielle felt she could not trust anybody out of fear of being killed. He had strategically groomed her, giving him full control over all aspects of her life. She had reached out for help others for help to no avail. Although, she did know firsthand experience with the police not helping. Her family refused involvement, and she had been isolated from all her loved ones. They blamed her. The mental stress he used by coaxing her led to her decision to move in with him. This was the biggest mistake of her life. Now, she has found herself in a desperate situation.

We never finished our lesson. My nonchalant attitude was disappearing, and I felt empathy for the young ladies sitting before me. I took all my notebooks home to look them over and discovered some hard facts. These young women wrote about little exposures that they had in their lives. Secondly, they lack the maturity to fully understand why gender bias plays a huge role in domestic abuse. Finally, these young ladies refused to believe that power and control could be confused with love.

Day 5 - Myth 3: The woman can walk away anytime.

This is one of the most common myths. A victim can't simply leave a relationship of domestic violence. The victim (usually a woman) must weigh the many factors involved in leaving the relationship. Fear, shame, normalization of abuse, intimidation, lack of resources, and low self-esteem all play into staying in an abusive relationship.

The facility had been closed for a week because of the renovation of the building. When the young ladies returned, it was difficult getting them to settle down until Ms. Cooper arrived. She walked into the room, and without a word, everyone quieted down. She gave me the signal to begin my session. I began my lesson with Myth 3, stating that a woman can walk anytime because I had just watched the movie, Enough. We watched a few clicks of the movie for discussion. I also knew that they hadn't had the security of being in class for a while, and there probably might have been a few episodes of violence during that time. I wanted them to understand that Slim, Jennifer Lopez's character was an example of what I pointed out in their last project. I emphasized that abuse was about power and control and that there are no limits to gender, race or class. I also demonstrated a plan to them to get away. The plan usually allows a person to think things through and examine all routes. We talked about the plan and Jennifer Lopez's struggles to get away and change her identity. We talked about her husband's desire to get her back and keep her in his control. Finally, we discussed her lack of resources and how these challenges can keep her self-esteem down and make many women stay. The continuous fighting to stay afloat is strenuous and can wear a person down. I wanted them to understand that a person in this situation must have faith and determination to break free. I wanted them to leave the class that day, respecting and understanding the survivors of abusive relationships.

When I looked in the back of the room, I noticed that Gabrielle seemed to be especially interested in what I was saying. When class was over, she stayed in her seat. After everyone else left, she just sat there. Ms. Cooper and I gave her space and worked on the upcoming lessons. There was no urgency for her to leave, but there seemed to be some serious problems that she was pondering over. We were allowed time to be to ourselves and hoped that she would either confide in us to get the obvious help she needed.

Gabrielle had pulled a chair by the window and stared outside at the parking lot. She was looking out for Arturo. Her weekend had been a nightmare of an experience, but she managed to run away. Arturo had been calling her repeatedly and leaving mixed messages on her phone. He made calls and persistently apologized. Then, he called back, screaming, cussing and threatening her life. He went by all of her friend's houses or called them. He didn't dare knock on her family's door. She reflected on the horrific incidents. It hurt her that no one at the family celebration would lift a finger or say a word to help her. She cried out, but his brothers, parents and friends listened to her call for help, saying it was a personal matter. It started at his family's barbeque. One of Arturo's friends, Gene, asked her a question, and Gabrielle answered and laughed. Arturo thought they were flirting with each other. He grabbed Gabrielle and dragged her to one of the bedrooms in the house. She resisted and yelled for help, but no one said a word. He locked the door, pushed her into a chair and accused her of going out with another guy. He held her captive until he heard what he wanted to. After denying the allegations several times, Arturo took it to another level. He slapped her and hit the back of the chair so hard that it knocked her to the floor. The music had been playing, and people were laughing and talking despite what she was going through. He drilled and drilled her as she was down on the floor. Then the music stopped, and people started to leave. He yelled at her to get up and stop acting like a baby. He commanded her to go wash her face. She waited for an opportunity that night and got away. She got an Uber and went to the nearest motel. That night she decided she had enough. Then the questions came to mind, how can she do this, and where can she go? She managed to get to class without him seeing her, but she still had no answers and didn't know who to trust. So, she was just staring out of the window.

One of the other girls came to Ms. Cooper before class that day and told her what happened to Gabrielle. When it came time for us to leave, Ms. Cooper went to her, hugged her then held her hand. At that point, Gabrielle broke down and cried. They talked, and Ms. Cooper sneaked her out the back door of the building and took her home with her. Gabrielle lay down in the car's back seat until they were completely out of the neighborhood. I waited a few minutes, turned out all the lights and went out the front door. I saw a car sitting on the far end of the lot. I turned and rode in the direction of the car. From there, you could not see the back door. When I felt it was safe, I drove close enough for him to see me get on the phone and point in his direction. I knew he would leave, and that's exactly what he did. I didn't realize what a chance I had taken until I got home. All I could do was sit on the couch and praise God.

Ms. Cooper lived alone. She was in the process of getting a divorce. She gave Gabrielle a room and towels so she could freshen up.

They agreed to get some rest and talk in the morning. The next morning after Gabrielle revealed her abused state, they decided to get help and send her away. The first thing they did was block all of Arturo's calls. To remove the anxiety of Arturo and his threats was to get rid of his voice and the fear it put into her. Ms. Cooper had a friend who lived outside the city who agreed to take Gabrielle in and help get her on her feet. Ms. Cooper allowed Gabrielle to stay at her house and relax for a couple of days. That weekend, she took Gabrielle to meet Ms. Jenkins, who was known for helping others in similar situations. They hit it off right away. When Ms. Cooper left, that would be the last time she would see Gabrielle.

By the time I completed my community work with the girls, most of the myths were covered. It was a surprise how the attitudes and connections between all involved in the sessions changed. Since the situation with Gabrielle happened, Ms. Cooper and I have emphasized the importance of watching out for one another.

Even Audrey and Charlene felt sorry for Gabrielle. After the class sessions, they had a better understanding of the position of women being abused. It seemed like God's plan for me was working out. Although, I admit I was glad this was almost over. I had a calendar on my refrigerator that I had been marking the days off.

My last day came, and the girls had planned a going away party. I went back to court. The judge congratulated me and said he read the rave reports about my work. He recommended that I consider working in the social service field. Afterwards, I headed to the center. The place was decorated beautifully. There was a table full of food. Who would have thought that these young ladies, with all of their issues, knew how to cook! Things were going so well, and I was on such a natural high. I was glad to have impacted the class in such a positive way. Ms. Cooper and I also grown to be good friends. She is the one who wrote me the glowing letter for the judge. As the party began to die down, and before anyone could say anything, Ms. Cooper announced, "As all of you know, I am a very private person," she said with a light laugh, then, "Well, I'm just going to put it bluntly1 I'm going on a vacation. I need relaxation and me time regardless of how much you think of me. I am not a superwoman." She laughed, and we all joined in. However, in the back of my mind, I felt something was wrong. Ms. Cooper told us she would be going to Italy for two weeks and bringing us souvenirs.

Two weeks passed, and I went to the center to see Ms. Cooper. I wanted to see if everything was okay. I at least wanted her to tell me about her trip. I arrived at the center around nine, expecting to see her car in the lot. I didn't see any cars around, but I waited for a while. At around 11:30 PM, the secretary came to the door and asked me to step out into the hall. She appeared to be very serious. A chill ran through my body, and I was afraid of what she was going to say. I put on a brave face and walked into the hall. I could see the tears in her eyes as she began to speak. She notified me that Ms. Cooper had been found dead in her house that morning. She had returned from her vacation, and her husband, who was hiding in the house, shot her. The shock was too much for me. I did not want to tell the others until the shock was too much for me. The secretary asked if I would make the announcement of Ms. Cooper's passing. I didn't want to tell the others until I got myself together. I went down the hall to the ladies' room and composed myself the best I could. I was all ready to tell the others now, but someone had already posted it on social media. The word spread, and I was now in the middle of emotional chaos.

No one had a clue that Ms. Cooper was also a victim of domestic abuse for many years. This was the reason why she worked so hard on the job to make sure that others would not have to experience the same pain. Her husband had lost contact with her when she went on vacation. He had been searching for her because she had gotten the divorce, and it was finalized. By the time she returned, his rage was uncontrollable because of his insecurities and the illusion that he lost Ms. Cooper to another man. He just shot her without saying a word. Confusion set in when he realized what he had done, and he didn't know what to do next. He ran, as far as he could. He reflected on the reality on his situation and his actions. Guilt and regret were killing his soul because he did truly love her. It was too much for him. So, he put the gun to his head and pulled the trigger.

She was given a beautiful memorial service. She had touched so many people's lives that about half the church was full of former clients, co-workers, and dignitaries. Flowers galore were all across the front of the huge church, and some were put in the side aisle. The minister only allowed a few to speak, and you could see the disappointment on so many faces who wanted to share their story and give thanks to this woman they loved so much. During the repast, they videoed everyone as a tribute to her. While I stood off to myself, the director came up to me. She offered her condolences and said she had a proposal for me. They now needed someone to take Ms. Cooper's position. She said that the judge had suggested that I would be a good candidate for the job.

Today, I will be receiving a new class of troubled young ladies. I remembered that God gave me this chance, and He knew what the outcome would be. He knows you are stronger than you think. God doesn't make mistakes. As I focused on my new journey, I thought about how it's not the size of the problem but how you deal with it. God has awesome plans for me. He is always there and knows the strength I have within me. I simply have to tell my enemies that I have the strength of God and I am here to accomplish the goals He put me here for. Therefore, I pray that I will be able to shake off the negative and deliver the positive to make changes in the lives of the women who came before me.

Comments:

Myths are the callous of misunderstanding, ignorance, and blaming the victims. The assumption that these myths are true has caused so many victims not to leave but endure because of shame. If you are a woman who has survived abuse, consider making your story known. Young people need to realize the danger of being in an abusive relationship. Telling your stories and dismantling the validity of myths can produce more informed women and revolutionize the awareness of domestic abuse.

This story demonstrates the fact that abuse doesn't pick a certain type of person, age, class or economic status. There is no prototype for who will experience domestic trauma in their life. The Bible says we all will experience some kind of trouble in our life. We need these episodes in order to grow and learn from our experiences. This is why we need to be more understanding of each other and exercise patience. Your problems may not be on the same level, and you may have dealt with the problems differently, but that doesn't make you any better or less than anyone else. Ms. Cooper is a good example. Although she helped young people to overcome their social problems, she never opened up about her own. She was an older, financially stable woman with the same issues in her life as her students. Ms. Cooper's death is still a teaching moment because it lets us see the worst scenario of abuse. Gabrielle is an example of a young woman who is confused and without hope. The young lady suffered bullying from her peers and family, resulting from people believing in the myths of abuse.

I pray that God will bless us to know when and what needs to be changed. Change has to be done by being more supportive of each other. Support starts with dismantling the myths about abuse victims and uplifting their spirits. Gossip, belittlement, and mistreatment of the victim isolates and produces more insecurities some women never overcome. Also, being more supportive of each other may be God's way for you to be a blessing to others. We are put on this earth in many different ways of handling and understanding our situations. It doesn't mean your perspective is better or worse than mine because God made each person with different talents, styles, trials and methods to get to the same place. The goal in this abuse case needs to be clarified, taught and explained. People from all walks of life need to clearly see that this is the way to plant the seed of wisdom. With this seed, it gives you the wisdom of knowledge. When God does a great thing in your life, you need to testify to somebody in the name of Jesus. This seed will help your awareness and make others aware of the things they need to see and hear happening in establishing relationships. This way, a person won't be completely blindsided. This seed will give you some solutions on dealing with problems and the insight to know that you are not alone. This seed will help to dispel the myths.

The Myths About Abuse

Myth:

If the abuse is a rare occurrence, it's not dangerous.

Myth Explanation:

All abuse is dangerous. Subtle aggression such as gaslighting, critical judgement, putdowns, and restrictions are all stepping stones to becoming more abusive in the future. A rare occurrence of abuse still controls the victim and sets the overall abusive dynamics in the relationship.

Myth:

Victims have certain types of personality traits or are a class of people that seek out abuse.

Myth Explanation:

No one type of person is a victim of abuse. Victims can come from any background, class, wealthy or poor. They do not have to have a personality disorder or mental illness to be susceptible to an abusive relationship. Abusers are the ones who are responsible for the abusive relationship.

Myth:

The woman can walk away at any time.

Myth Explanation:

One of the most common myths, a victim isn't able to simply leave a relationship of domestic violence. The victim (usually a woman) must weigh the many factors in leaving the relationship. Fear, shame, normalization of abuse, intimidation, lack of resources, and low self-esteem play into staying in an abusive relationship.

Victims must have a safety plan, resources and support, a safe place to go and the ability to financially care for themselves. Even if the victim leaves, there's a high chance she will return, as the abuser will use more tactics to keep her in the cycle of abuse; love bombing, promises to change, and harsh threats.

Having a concrete plan in place will help her be as safe as possible. Having a strong support system will help her stay out of the relationship.

Myth:

Just because a person is physically abusive once doesn't mean they will do it again.

Myth Explanation:

At first incident of physical abuse doesn't start with the abuser physically abusing his victim. There are other signs and steps that the abuser shows beforehand.

Most domestic violence starts with subtle forms of emotional abuse, which are looked at as criticism toward the victim. The abuser slowly escalates over time. It's like a frog in a pot of water on the stove. The frog doesn't realize it's being boiled when the heat slowly turns up.

Myth:

Domestic abuse happens because he loses his temper or drinks too much.

Myth Explanation:

Abusers make conscious decisions on who, how, and when to abuse. Drinking or other habits can exacerbate violence, but it's not the cause of the abuse and is only an excuse for their irreprehensible behavior.

Domestic abuse isn't about a person who's unable to control their feelings but rather about controlling the victim by striking fear into them.

Myth:

If the abuser apologizes and is truly sorry, they won't do it again,

Myth Explanation:

Apologies after an episode of abuse is one of many ways the abuser manipulates the victim with abuse. It is meant to create confusion and control the victim to stay in the relationship.

Myth:

Domestic abuse is a family problem, a couple's problem, or a relationship problem.

Myth Explanation:

Domestic abuse is a cultural and societal problem. To believe it is a dynamic relationship plays into blaming the victim. The victim, including children and other family members, should not be blamed for the abuse. The abuser should be the one who takes the responsibility.

Myth:

Domestic abuse doesn't affect very many people.

Myth Explanation:

Domestic abuse is considered the most common yet least reported crime. Why? Because our culture blames the victim as well as the abuser.

Our society does not treat domestic abuse as a crime but rather as a relationship problem. Abusers do not generally get punished in the legal system, and victims do not have the resources as not the support needed to help them leave a relationship.

These are some of many of the myths of domestic abuse and violence. The only way to topple these myths is to read, research, and learn more about the dynamics of intimate partner violence. If more people understand these tactics and work to fight against them, we can get the control out of the abuser's hands.

Statistical Facts

On average, nearly 20 people per minute are physically abused by an intimate partner in the United States. During one year, this equates to more than 10 million women and men; 1 in 4 women and 1 in 9 men experience severe intimate partner physical violence, intimate partner contacts sexual violence, and/or intimate partner stalking with impacts such as injury, fearfulness, post-traumatic, stress disorder, use of victim services, and/or contraction of sexually transmitted diseases.

- 1 in 3 women and 1in 4 men have experienced some form of physical violence by an intimate partner. This includes a range of behaviors (e.g., slapping, shoving, pushing) and, in some cases, might not be considered "domestic violence."

- 1 in 7 women and 1 in 25 men have been injured by an intimate partner.
- 1 in 10 women has been raped by an intimate partner. Data is unavailable on male victims.
- 1 in 4 and 1 in 7 men have been victims of severe physical violence (e.g., beating, burning, strangling) by an intimate partner in their lifetime.
- 1 in 7 women and 1 in 18 men have been stalked by an intimate partner during their lifetime to the point in which they felt very fearful or believed that they or someone close to them would be harmed or killed.
- On a typical day, more than 20,000 phone calls are placed to domestic violence hotlines nationwide.
- The presence of a gun in a domestic violence situation increases the risk of homicide by 5000%.
- Intimate partner violence accounts for 15% of all violent crimes.

- Women between the ages of 18-24 are most commonly abused by an intimate partner.
- 19% of domestic violence involves a weapon.
- Domestic victimization is correlated with a higher rate of depression and suicidal behavior.
- Only 34% of people whose intimate partners injure, receive medical care for their injuries.

Rape: Rape is defined as committing unlawful sexual intercourse with a person, without consent, usually through force or intimidation. A lack of consent can include the victim's inability to say "no" to intercourse because of intoxication from drugs or alcohol.

- 1 in 5 women and 1 in 71 men in the United States have been raped in their lifetime.
- Almost half of female (46.7%) and male (44.9%) victims of rape in the United States were raped by an acquaintance. Of these, 45.4% of female rape victims and 29% of

male rape victims were raped by an intimate partner.

Stalking: The act or crime of willingly and repeatedly following or harassing another person in circumstances that cause a reasonable person to fear injury or death, especially because of express if implied threats. This crime of engaging in the course of conduct directed at a person that serves no legitimate purpose and seriously alarms, annoys or intimidates that person. It can result in getting a restraining order to protect the victim.

- 19.3 million women and 5.1 million men in the United States have been stalked in their lifetime. 60.8% of female stalking victims and 43.5% of men reported being stalked by a current or former intimate partner.

Homicide: A killing of one human being by another.

- A study of intimate partner homicides found that 20% of victims were not the intimate partners themselves but family members, friends, neighbors, persons who intervened, law enforcement responders or bystanders.
- 72% of all murder suicides involve an intimate partner; 94% of the victims of these murder-suicides are females.

On average, nearly 20 people per minute are physically abused by an intimate partner in the United States. During a year, that equates to more than 10 million women and men. Women are more likely than men to be the victim of their intimate male counterparts. Statistics also show that the more common victims are women between the ages of 18-24. The things not talked about are the lessons learned, how people have overcome them, and the impact they may have on women for the rest of their lives. Daughters are not being prepared for the likelihood that this could happen to them. Young women are walking into relationships unaware of the signs to look for and not understanding that there are ways of getting out of these toxic relationships. Cutting All Ties is about women who survived their abusive situations and how they broke away and cut ties that held them there. This book talks about various ranges of abuse when women lost all hope but the strength and willingness to make that move to leave. The stories and poems are part nonfiction because they are based on real cases from grandmothers, mothers, aunts, older female neighbors and older siblings. Although these stories were based on real life and the victims, most importantly, survived, these were written to inspire the young to reach for the best in life.

South Suburban Domestic Violence Training:
Crisis Center for South Suburban (1979)

www.crisisctr.org

National Coalition Against Domestic Violence:
http://ncadv.org

Acknowledgments

First and foremost, I thank you, God, for always being there. You are my true inspiration. I can hear your whispers saying, "Ask, and you shall receive." In my prayers and private conversations, it was You who brought me through my troubling times.

Secondly, Annyce Dunbar, you covered three roles: first, as my mother; second, as my mentor; and third, as my best friend. You always encouraged me as my mother. We had an understanding that we could agree to disagree at times without drama. It also allowed us to have an open and advise each other. You encourage me to finish school and fulfill my dreams. Although she didn't live to see this in print, I have to thank her for everything.

My son, Ronald and Lawrence, constantly encourage me through positive reinforcement by telling of my strengths, resilience, and confidence in uplifting my self-esteem. They see more in me now than I could ever imagine. Again, thank you both and pray for inner strength and creativity to soar beyond our dreams.

I would like to thank Dr. Janice Fortman for encouraging me to complete my book. You inspired me as an exemplary Toastmaster and writer. I give kudos to my cousins Joyce Hutchinson, Kevin Reed and Terry Reed and my inspiring brothers, Larry Dunbar and Gus Dunbar. To my godmother, Ms. Rose Anderson, who is my life supporter. I would also like to thank my colleagues Janice Randall, Katherine

Buchanan, Laroma White esq., Dr. Sandra Inniss, and Charnae Ross, who constantly remind me to complete what I started. Next, I can't forget my extraordinary angels, Darrick Alexander and Brenda Harris. I wish I had completed this project in time for them to see it. Finally, I would like to thank all the women willing to share their stories.

I will always remember that fear ends where faith begins.

About the Author

Gwendolyn Dunbar is an educator, historian, mentor, writer, public speaker, and author of her first book, *Cutting the Ties.*

She has continued to be an educator for Chicago Public Schools for more than three decades. With a Bachelor of Art degree in History, Master of Art degree in Elementary Education and in Educational Leadership, she has a strong passion to form a pact between the generations of women to exchange their experiences with each other. Gwendolyn gains her strength from her sons who continue to support and encouragement her. She is urging the public to learn more about the prevention of abuse and to make others aware of the signs of abuse. Her short stories, poems, and words of wisdom are written to inspire the reader to be empathetic to older, mature women who have survived abuse. The stories will hopefully open the minds of the younger generation to be aware of the pitfalls, signs, and destruction of getting in and out of abusive relationships.

Printed in the USA
CPSIA information can be obtained
at www.ICGtesting.com
CBHW070057170224
4317CB00006B/23

9 781916 964983